The Essential Workbook for

Geometry

유하림(Harim Yoo) 지음

Preface

To. 학부모님과 학생들께

The Essential Workbook for Geometry의 출간에 앞서, 이전에 출간된 교재를 구매해주신 학부모님과 학생들에게 진심으로 감사의 말씀을 전하고자 합니다. 핵심 개념 교재들을 꾸준히 구매해주신 학부모님과 학생들 덕분에, 후속편으로 문제풀이편을 작업할 수 있는 원동력을 유지할 수 있었습니다. 이 교재는 Geometry 교과 개념편인 The Essential Guide to Geometry의 후속편이라고 볼 수 있는 교재로, 두 가지 측면을 생각하며 집필하였습니다.

첫째, how보다 why에 집중하며 썼습니다. '왜 이 개념을 사용해야하지?'라는 생각을 필두로, 문제풀이에서 학생들이 개념의 본질을 볼 수 있도록 노력하였으며, 이를 푸는 학생들이 why에 집중해서 공부하다보면, 문제의 유형이 아닌, 개념의 본질을 이해하는데 성공적일 것이라고 믿고 있습니다. 둘째, 교과서에서 볼 수 있는 문제보다 조금 더 난이도 있는 문제들을 공부함으로써, 학교 내신에서도 좋은 성적을 거둘 수 있도록 집필하였습니다. 또한, 이 내용들이 경시 수학에서도 그대로 이어질 수 있도록, AMC 8/10/12에서도 soft-landing 할 수 있길 바라며 집필에 힘썼습니다.

이 교재를 출간할 수 있도록 '롤모델'로써 '강사'로써 성장할 수 있는 원동력을 주시는 심현성 대표님께 감사합니다. 또한, 이런 집필의 기회를 마련해주신 마스터프렙 권주근 대표님께 감사합니다. 또한, 현재 제 여러 교재 검수를 맡고 있는 든든한 안준규 제자, 그리고 꼼꼼한 검수를 봐주신 이화익 선생님께 감사의 마음을 전합니다. 언제나 든든한 지원군인 제 아내와 딸, 부모님께도 항상 감사합니다. 마지막으로, 제 삶에 이러한 기회를 주신 하나님께 감사드립니다. 앞으로도 더 좋은 교재를 만들어 견고하고 튼튼한 유하림 커리큘럼을 완성하겠습니다.

2023년 1월
유하림

저자 소개

유하림(Harim Yoo)

미국 Northwestern University,
B.A. in Mathematics and Economics
(**노스웨스턴 대학교 수학과/경제학과 졸업**)

마스터프렙 수학영역 대표강사
압구정 현장강의 ReachPrep 원장

[저 서]
몰입공부
The Essential Guide to Prealgebra
The Essential Guide to Algebra 1
The Essential Guide to Geometry
The Essential Guide to Algebra 2
The Essential Guide to Precalculus
The Essential Workbook for SAT Math Level 2
The Essential Guide to SAT Math Level 2
The Essential Guide to IGCSE : Addmath
The Essential Guide to Competition Math (Fundamentals)
The Essential Guide to Number Theory (Competition Math)
The Essential Guide to Counting and Probability (Competition Math)

이 책의 특징

유하림 커리큘럼 Essential Math Series의 개념 교재 학습 이후 공부하면 좋은 문제풀이편 교재입니다. 개념 공부는 한번 끝난 학생들을 위한 교재로 적합하게 쓰이길 희망하며 집필하였습니다. 명문 Junior Boarding School 및 Boarding School을 진학하고, 교내에서 좋은 GPA를 유지하기에 필요한 내용들을 모두 포함하고자 힘썼으며, 7, 8학년에게 필요한 문제풀이 교재로, 현장강의 학생들에게 직접 적용하며, 피드백을 받아가며 작성한 교재입니다.

 ## 기본에 충실한 책

유하림 커리큘럼 Essential Math Series의 개념편에서 설명한 내용들을 토대로 작성하였으며, 학교에서 배우는 개념에 생각하는 과정을 입히기 위해 한문제 한문제 풀 때마다, 배운 개념을 떠올리고 복습하기 위해 좋은 문제들을 자체제작하여, 공부하는 학생들이 100% 이상의 효과를 낼 수 있도록 집필하였습니다.

 ## 생각의 확장을 위한 책

How보다 Why에 집중한 교재로, 왜 이 개념이 여기에서 적용되는지, 한 개념을 바라볼 때, 어떠한 마음가짐으로 봐야하는지, 개념의 본질에 집중하도록 제작한 문제들로 구성된 교재입니다. 말 그대로, 생각의 확장을 위한 교재로 교과 Geometry뿐 아니라, 경시 Geometry에서도 적용이 가능한 생각의 씨앗을 품기 위한 교재로 활용하길 바랍니다.

CONTENTS

유하림 커리큘럼으로 **Geometry** 공부하는 방법

개념 학습 + 문제 풀이

 The Essential Guide to Geometry 개념 학습을 완성합니다.

 The Essential Workbook for Geometry 문제풀이를 답지를 보지 않은 상태로 풀어봅니다.

 The Essential Workbook for Geometry 답지에 나온 풀이와 자신의 풀이를 비교하며, 개념의 공백 부분을 채워넣고, 알고 있 는 부분에는 확신을 가집니다.

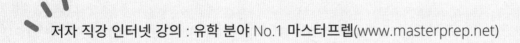 저자 직강 인터넷 강의 : 유학 분야 No.1 마스터프렙(www.masterprep.net)

Part 1

---

150 Problems for Geometry

in multiple-choice forms

001. Point / Line / Plane

Which of the following is the most appropriate word that could go inside the empty parentheses?

A plane can be illustrated as a (   ) surface, containing infinitely many points and infinitely extending without any boundary.

(A) curved
(B) flat
(C) wobbly
(D) spiraling

002. Definition of Plane

How many <u>planes</u> will contain three collinear points, as shown in the figure below?

(A) 0 plane
(B) 1 plane
(C) 2 planes
(D) infinitely many planes

003. Counting in Geometry

How many different segments can be formed if the endpoints of a given segment must be selected out of these four vertices of a square shown in the figure below? (In this problem, two segments located in different positions are to be considered distinct, even if they are congruent.)

(A) 4
(B) 5
(C) 6
(D) 7

004. Counting in Geometry

How many distinct segments can be formed if the endpoints of a given segment must be selected out of these six vertices of a regular hexagon shown in the figure below? (In this problem, two congruent segments located in different positions are considered indistinct.)

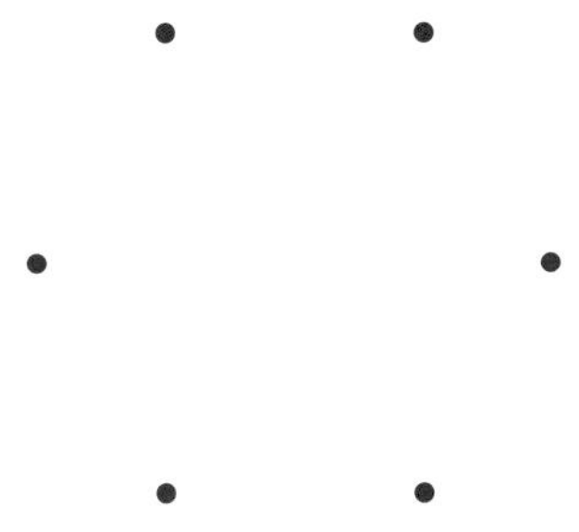

(A) 1
(B) 2
(C) 3
(D) 4

If points A, B, C, and D are all coplanar[1] points, while $\overline{AB}$ and $\overline{CD}$ are congruent, where $AB = 2x - 1$ and $CD = 3x - 4$, find $AB + CD$.
(A) 3
(B) 5
(C) 6
(D) 10

If points A, B, C, and D are all coplanar points, and if $AB = 3 - 2x$ and $CD = 3x - 7$, which of the following is true about the statement that "$\overline{AB} \cong \overline{CD}$?"
(A) it is true for $x = 2$.
(B) it is true for all values of x.
(C) it is true for some value of x other than $x = 2$.
(D) it is false.

---

[1]Points are called coplanar if they are on the same plane

007. Distance Formula using Ratio - Part 1.

Find the coordinate of C, if there exists a point C between A and B on a real number line such that $AC : CB = 2 : 3$, $A = 5$ and $B = 10$.

(A) 6

(B) 7

(C) 8

(D) 9

008. Distance Formula using Ratio - Part 2.

On a line containing A and B shown in the figure below, there are two possible locations for point C such that $AC : CB = 2 : 3$, which is not shown in the figure. If the coordinates of A and B are 2 and 12, respectively, compute the sum of all possible coordinates of C.

A B

(A) 0

(B) 6

(C) 12

(D) −12

Compute the area of a triangle formed by $(3,3)$, $(1,1)$ and $(2,5)$.

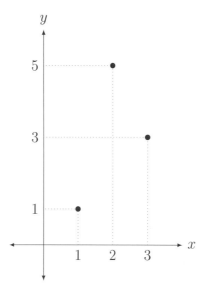

(A) 1.5   (B) 2   (C) 2.5   (D) 3

Compute the area of a quadrilateral formed by $(-1,1)$, $(1,3)$, $(2,-1)$, and $(4,2)$.
(A) 10.5
(B) 11
(C) 11.5
(D) 2

011. Distance Formula (Euclidean Metric) - Part 1.

Compute the distance between two points $A(1,2)$ and $B(4,6)$, using the usual Euclidean formula[2], i.e.,

$$d((x_1, y_1), (x_2, y_2)) = \sqrt{(x_1 - x_2)^2 + (y_1 - y_2)^2}$$

(A) 5
(B) 7
(C) 8
(D) 10

012. Distance Formula (Taxicab Metric) - Part 2.

Unlike the usual distance formula we use, there is a distance notion called "taxicab metric." Think about the a taxi that can only travel along the roads that are either horizontal or vertical. Here is the formula

$$d((x_1, y_1), (x_2, y_2)) = |x_1 - x_2| + |y_1 - y_2|$$

Compute the distance using taxicab metric between two points $A(4, 2)$ and $B(1, -2)$.

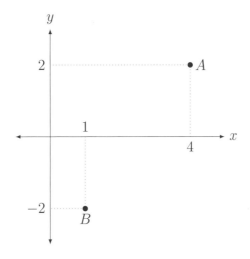

(A) 5   (B) 7   (C) 8   (D) 10

---

[2]Here, $d((x_1, y_1), (x_2, y_2))$ stands for the distance between two points with coordinates (x_1, y_1) and (x_2, y_2).

013. Distance Formula (Space Extension) - Part 3.

A point in space (x, y, z) can be demonstrated as a point (x, y) in the regular xy plane that is lifted to zth floor. For instance, if there is a point $(1, 1, 2)$, then this must be a point $(1, 1)$ in the regular xy plane that is in the 2nd floor, as shown in the figure below. Compute the distance[3] between $O(0, 0, 0)$ and $A(1, 1, 2)$.

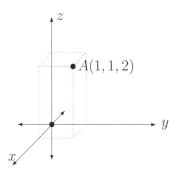

(A) 2
(B) $\sqrt{5}$
(C) $\sqrt{6}$
(D) $\sqrt{7}$

014. Distance Formula (Space Extension) - Part 4.

Find the distance between two points in space $(1, 2, 3)$ and $(3, 4, 6)$.
(A) $\sqrt{15}$
(B) $\sqrt{17}$
(C) $\sqrt{19}$
(D) $\sqrt{21}$

---

[3]We normally denote the origin as O, and $O(0, 0, 0)$ indicates the point of intersection among x, y, and z-axes.

015. Definition of Complementary Angles

If adjacent angles A and B are complementary such that $m\angle A = 30° - x$ and $m\angle B = 45° + 2x$, compute the value of x.
(A) 5°
(B) 10°
(C) 15°
(D) 20°

016. Definition of Angle Bisectors

In a plane, "two perpendicular lines" must be the locus[4] of points equidistant from
(A) a point
(B) a circle
(C) a line
(D) two intersecting lines

[4] the set of points traced, satisfying the given condition.

017. Locus of Plane Intersections

Which of the following could be the intersection of three distinct planes in space?
(A) a straight line
(B) exactly two points
(C) a plane
(D) exactly three points

018. Locus of Plane Intersections

A straight line can be determined by at least
(A) one point
(B) two distinct points
(C) three distinct points
(D) four distinct points

019. True/False Questions

Determine the truth value of the following statements.

(a) Non-adjacent angles A and B can be complementary. (T/F)

(b) A linear pair must be both adjacent and supplementary. (T/F)

(c) Three points determine a unique plane. (T/F)

(d) Two lines that are not parallel to each other must intersect at a point. (T/F)

(e) Two distinct planes in space that are not parallel to each other must intersect at a line. (T/F)

(f) There are infinitely many lines passing through two points. (T/F)

020. Conditional Statements

Determine the truth value of the following conditional statements.

(a) "Given a real number x, if $x^2 = 3$, then $x = \sqrt{3}$." (T/F)

(b) "If x is a real number then $x^2 = -1$." (T/F)

(c) "If $x = 1$, then $x^2 = 1$." (T/F)

(d) "If $x^2 \neq 1$, then $x \neq 1$." (T/F)

(e) "If $x^2 = 1$, then $x = 1$." (T/F)

(f) "If $x \neq 1$, then $x^2 \neq 1$." (T/F)

021. Segment Addition Postulate - Part 1.

Given two points A and B, if C is between A and B, which of the following must be true?
(A) $AC = BC$.
(B) $AC + BC = AB$.
(C) $\overline{AC} + \overline{BC} = \overline{AB}$.
(D) $\overline{AC} = \overline{BC}$.

022. Segment Addition Postulate - Part 2. / Triangular Inequality

Given two points A and B, if C is not on the line containing A and B, which of the following must be true?
(A) $AC + BC < AB$.
(B) $AC + BC = AB$.
(C) $AC + BC > AB$.
(D) $AC = BC$.

Three points A, B, and C are on a real number line in the written order. If $A = 3$, $C = 10$, and $AB : BC = 4 : 7$, then the coordinate of B equals m/n where m and n are relatively prime. Compute $m + n$.

(A) 61

(B) 72

(C) 83

(D) 94

If $\overrightarrow{AD}$ bisects $\angle BAC$, where $m\angle BAD = (2x - 10)°$ and $m\angle BAC = (3x + 1)°$, compute the measure of $\angle DAC$.

(A) $30°$

(B) $31°$

(C) $32°$

(D) $33°$

025. Distance between a Point and a Line

Compute the distance between a point $(3, 4)$ and $y = x$.

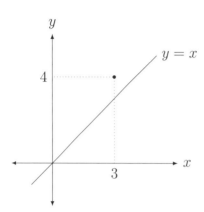

(A) 1 (B) $\sqrt{2}$ (C) $\dfrac{\sqrt{2}}{2}$ (D) $\dfrac{1}{2}$

026. Distance between a Line and a Line

If the square of the distance between two lines $y = 2x + 1$ and $y = 2x - 3$ can be written as $\dfrac{m}{n}$ where m and n are relatively positive integers, compute $m + n$.

(A) 15
(B) 17
(C) 19
(D) 21

If $A(1,1)$, $B(3,1)$ and $C(3,3)$, compute the area of the triangle bounded by three points.

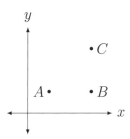

(A) $\sqrt{2}$
(B) 2
(C) $\sqrt{3}$
(D) 4

If $A(0,0)$, $B(2,1)$ and $C(1,5)$, compute the area of the triangle bounded by three points.

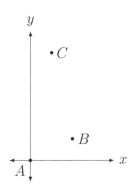

(A) $\dfrac{7}{2}$ (B) 4   (C) $\dfrac{9}{2}$ (D) 5

029. Interior Angle Theorem + Number Theory

If the interior angles of a triangle form an arithmetic sequence, where the measures of each angle are distinct integers, find out the total number of distinct triangles satisfying the given condition.
(A) 59
(B) 60
(C) 61
(D) 62

030. Exterior Angle Theorem

Compute the measure of exterior angle when two remote angles have the measures of $41 - 2x$ and $2x + 43$, for some valid values of x.
(A) 84
(B) 88
(C) 92
(D) 96

031. Special Points in Circle - Part 1.

The center of the circle circumscribed about a triangle can be found by drawing
(A) perpendicular bisectors of sides.
(B) angle bisectors of interior angles.
(C) altitudes to the sides.
(D) medians of the triangle.

032. Special Points in Circle - Part 2.

The center of the circle inscribed in a triangle can be found by
(A) perpendicular bisectors of sides.
(B) angle bisectors of interior angles.
(C) altitudes to the sides.
(D) medians of the triangle.

033. Congruence Postulates

Which of the following answer choices does NOT guarantee a true statement?

Two triangles are congruent if

(A) two corresponding sides and one corresponding angle are congruent to one another.
(B) three corresponding sides are congruent to one another.
(C) two corresponding angles and one corresponding side are congruent to one another.
(D) they are similar with equal areas.

034. Sum of Exterior Angles

The sum of exterior angles of a polygon with three sides, as shown in the figure below, is

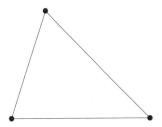

(A) 180°
(B) 360°
(C) 540°
(D) 720°

035. Segment Congruence Conditions

Which of the following choices does NOT make a true statement?

Two line segments are congruent if

(A) they are corresponding sides of two congruent triangles.
(B) they are two sides of a rhombus.
(C) they are chords of a same circle equidistant from the center.
(D) they are corresponding sides of two similar triangles.

036. Tangents

Given a point X and a circle centered at O, where X is not on the circle O, if one of the tangents has the length of 5, and the other tangent $3x - 1$, compute the value of x.
(A) 0
(B) 2
(C) 4
(D) 6

037. Special Isosceles Triangle

Assume there are two triangles $\triangle ABC$ and $\triangle DEF$ where $\triangle ABC$ is an isosceles triangle whose vertex angle measures $60°$ and $\triangle DEF$ is equilateral. Then, $\triangle ABC$ and $\triangle DEF$ are

(A) congruent to each other.

(B) obtuse.

(C) similar to each other.

(D) equal in area.

038. A.I.A Theorem

Assume there are three lines p, q, and r in the same plane. If p and q are parallel, and r is the transversal that cuts through these two lines, then alternate interior angle pairs formed are

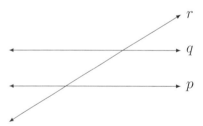

(A) complementary.

(B) supplementary.

(C) congruent.

(D) not congruent.

A sphere is a three-dimensional figure(in fact, a surface of a ball), completely round, all points of which are equidistant from a fixed point called center. If such distance is r, the volume of a sphere of radius r is given by

(A) $V = \dfrac{1}{3}\pi r^3$ (B) $V = 4\pi r^3$ (C) $V = \dfrac{4}{3}\pi r^3$ (D) $V = \dfrac{4}{3}\pi r^2$

040. Intersection between Circles

Assume there are two circles centered at two coplanar points A and B such that the circle with center A has radius 5 and one with center B has radius 4. If $AB = 9$, compute the maximum number of intersection points between the two figures.
(A) 0
(B) 1
(C) 2
(D) 3

041. Triangular Inequality

Given three coplanar points, A, B, and C, if $\overline{AB} \perp \overline{BC}$, which of the following must be true?

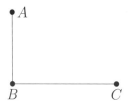

(A) $AB < BC$ (B) $AB = BC$ (C) $AB < AC$ (D) $AC < AB$

042. Externally Tangent Circles / Pythagorean Theorem

Given two circles ω_A and ω_B centered at A and B, respectively, if the two circles are externally tangent at point R such that $AR = 5$ and $BR = 2$, there exists an external tangent PQ such that P is on ω_A and Q on ω_B. If the internal tangent passing through R meets $\overline{PQ}$ at S, determine PS.
(A) $\sqrt{5}$
(B) $\sqrt{10}$
(C) $\sqrt{15}$
(D) $2\sqrt{5}$

043. Isosceles Triangle

If a triangle ABC is an isosceles triangle such that $AB = AC$, then
(A) the altitudes has the measure of one third of the base.
(B) the bisectors of the base angles are congruent.
(C) the base angles are complementary.
(D) all three angles are congruent.

044. Regular Polygon

The sum of measures of all interior angles of a regular pentagon is
(A) 180°
(B) 360°
(C) 540°
(D) 1080°

In the following figure, if $AM = MB$, $BN = NC$ and $AC = 8$, then $MN =$

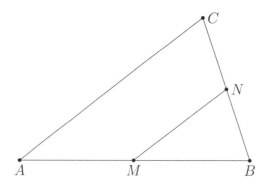

(A) 1
(B) 2
(C) 3
(D) 4

The set of vertices (other than those at the base side) of all isosceles triangles in a plane having a given segment $\overline{AB}$ as base is contained in
(A) a circle.
(B) a line.
(C) an ellipse.
(D) a ray.

047. Diagonals in Quadrilaterals

If the diagonals of a quadrilateral *bisect* each other, then the quadrilateral is generally known as a

(A) square.

(B) rhombus.

(C) trapezoid.

(D) parallelogram.

048. Diagonals in Quadrilaterals

If the line L intersects a circle of radius r at two distinct points, let's say A and B, then it is known as a *secant* line. (Refer to the following figure. If the bottom point is A, then the top point is B.) Then, the measure of segment $\overline{AB}$ is

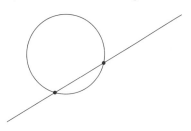

(A) less than $2r$.

(B) less than or equal to $2r$.

(C) equal to $2r$.

(D) greater than or equal to $2r$.

049. Locus

The locus of all points which lie inside or on a circle C and are equidistant from two given points on C is

(A) a chord of C which does not necessarily contain the center of C.

(B) a radius of C.

(C) a circle concentric with C.

(D) a diameter of C.

050. Lines of Symmetry

How many lines in a square are symmetric?

(A) 1

(B) 2

(C) 3

(D) 4

051. Regular Polygon

The sum of measures of the exterior angles of a regular polygon having 12 sides made by producing each of the sides in succession is
(A) 120°
(B) 180°
(C) 360°
(D) 1200°

052. Altitudes / Similar Triangles

If $\triangle ABC$ has a right angle at vertex C, then the altitude from vertex B
(A) separates $\triangle ABC$ into two similar triangles.
(B) separates $\triangle ABC$ into two congruent triangles.
(C) is congruent to $\overline{BC}$.
(D) is perpendicular to side $\overline{AB}$.

053. Circle Area / Circumference

If the circumference of a circle is 4 inches, then the closest integer to the area of circle equals
(A) 1
(B) 2
(C) 3
(D) 4

054. Space Geometry Terminology

Which of the following is the most equivalent to the shape of a parallelepiped?
(A) polygon.
(B) rectangle.
(C) prism.
(D) pyramid.

055. Equidistant Condition

The point (in the plane) which is equidistant from all three vertices of a right triangle is
(A) intersection of the medians.
(B) intersection of the altitudes.
(C) intersection of (interior) angle bisectors.
(D) intersection of the perpendicular bisectors of the sides.

056. Lines in Space

Two lines in space are parallel if
(A) they are both perpendicular to the same line.
(B) they are both parallel to the same line.
(C) they are both parallel to the same plane.
(D) they do not intersect.

The contrapositive of the statement "If A, then B" is the statement
(A) If not A, then not B.
(B) If B, then A.
(C) If not B, then not A.
(D) If not B, then A.

A regular tetrahedron of side length of 2 has a volume of $\frac{a\sqrt{b}}{c}$ where a, b and c are positive integers such that b is square-free. If a and c are relatively prime, which of the following equals $a + b + c$?
(A) 6
(B) 7
(C) 8
(D) 9

059. Planes in Space

Two distinct planes, perpendicular to the same plane, cannot be
(A) parallel.
(B) perpendicular.
(C) identical.
(D) orthogonal.

060. Angles in Circles

If points A, B, and D lie on a circle with center C so that $\angle ACB$ and $\angle ADB$ intercept the same arc, then the ratio of $m\angle ACB$ to $m\angle ADB$ equals

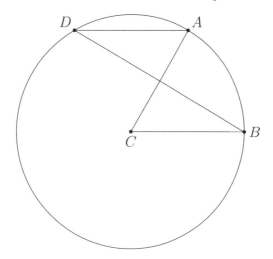

(A) $\dfrac{1}{2}$ (B) 1   (C) 2   (D) 4

As shown in the figure below, if $ABCD$ is a trapezoid with $BE = 16$, $AD = 5$, $DE = 4$ and $DC = 10$, then the area of $ABCD$ (in square units) is

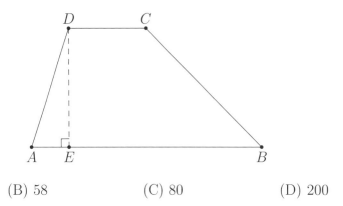

(A) 39   (B) 58   (C) 80   (D) 200

The set of all points in space which are equidistant from a straight line can be described as
(A) a pyramid with infinite height.
(B) a sphere with infinite radius.
(C) a cylinder with infinite height.
(D) a prism with infinite height.

063. Tangency

If $\overline{AB}$ and $\overline{BC}$ are tangent to the circle with center O at points A and C respectively, and $m\angle ABC = 120°$ and $OB = 12$, then the length of the segment $\overline{AB}$ equals

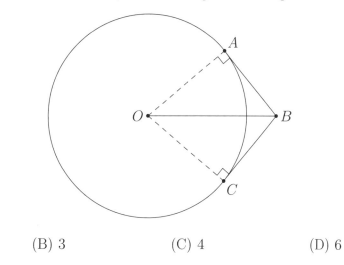

(A) 2   (B) 3   (C) 4   (D) 6

064. Similar Figures / Squares

If $ABCD$ and $BDEF$ are squares, and the area of $ABCD$ is 3 square inches, then the area of $BDEF$ equals

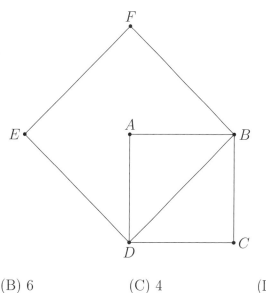

(A) $2\sqrt{3}$ (B) 6   (C) 4   (D) $3\sqrt{2}$

If diameter $\overline{AB}$ has measure 18, $\overline{MN} \perp \overline{AB}$ and $NB = 8$, then $MB =$

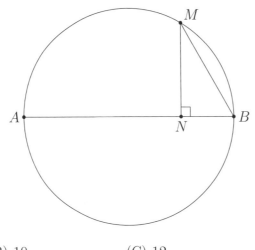

(A) 8   (B) 10   (C) 12   (D) 14

One angle of a rhombus has measure 120°. If the shorter diagonal has measure 12 inches, then the measure of a side of the rhombus is
(A) 12 inches.
(B) $4\sqrt{3}$ inches.
(C) 13 inches.
(D) $12\sqrt{3}$ inches.

067. Conditional Statements

Given the statements

p: if a man lives in Chicago, he lives in Illinois.

q: if a man does not live in Chicago, he does not live in Illinois.

(A) p and q have the same conclusions.

(B) p and q have the same hypothesis.

(C) q is the inverse of p.

(D) q is the converse of p.

068. Definition of Midpoints

If X is the midpoint of $\overline{AB}$, then

(A) A is on ray $\overrightarrow{XB}$.

(B) $\overrightarrow{XB}$ and $\overrightarrow{BX}$ represent the same ray.

(C) $\overline{AX} + \overline{XB} = \overleftrightarrow{AB}$.

(D) $AX = XB$.

069. Lines and Planes

How many distinct planes are determined by any two of four different parallel lines in space, no three of which lie in the same plane?
(A) 2
(B) 4
(C) 6
(D) 8

070. Pythagoras Theorem

If the hypotenuse of a right triangle is 10 inches and one of the acute angles is 60°, then the length of one leg must be
(A) 5
(B) $5\sqrt{2}$
(C) 6
(D) 8

071. Cyclic Quadrilateral

Find the area of a square inscribed in a circle of radius 2.
(A) $2\sqrt{2}$ square units
(B) $\sqrt{2}$ square units
(C) 2 square units
(D) 8 square units

072. Pythagoras Theorem

If $\triangle FQD$ is an equilateral triangle in which $\overline{QM}$ is perpendicular to $\overline{FD}$, then which one of the following assertions is true?
(A) $QF^2 + QD^2 = QM^2$
(B) $FM^2 + MD^2 = QD^2$
(C) $[QFD] = (FD) \cdot (QM)$
(D) $QM^2 = 3/4 \cdot QF^2$

073. Point / Line / Plane in Space

At a point on a line in space, how many lines can be drawn perpendicular to the line?
(A) 0
(B) 1
(C) 2
(D) infinitely many

074. Midpoint Formula in Plane

The midpoint of the line segment whose endpoints are $(-7, 6)$ and $(3, -4)$ has the coordinates
(A) $(6, 3)$
(B) $(2, -1)$
(C) $(-2, 1)$
(D) $(7, -4)$

075. Similarity

Given a triangle $\triangle ABC$, D and F are the midpoints of $\overline{AB}$ and $\overline{AC}$, respectively, which one of the following statements is true?
(A) The area of $\triangle ADF$ is one eighth the area of $\triangle ABC$.
(B) $\triangle ADF$ is isosceles.
(C) $DF = 1/3 \cdot BC$.
(D) $\overline{DF} \parallel \overline{BC}$ and $2 \cdot DF = BC$.

076. Altitudes / Similarities

Given a right triangle $\triangle MQP$ with right angle at Q. K is the foot of the altitude from Q to $\overline{MP}$. All except one statement are true. Which of the following is false?
(A) $\dfrac{MK}{QK} = \dfrac{QK}{PK}$.
(B) $\dfrac{MP}{MQ} = \dfrac{MQ}{MK}$.
(C) $\dfrac{QP}{MP} = \dfrac{KP}{QP}$.
(D) $KP^2 = QK^2 + QP^2$.

077. Power of Points / Similarity

Consider a circle O with chords $\overline{AB}$ and $\overline{CD}$ intersecting at S. If $AS = 2$, $SB = 3$, and $SD = 4$, then $SC =$
(A) 1
(B) 3/2
(C) 2
(D) 5/2

078. Altitudes

A point moves such that the sum of the squares of its distances from two given fixed lines, which are perpendicular to each other, is always the same positive number. What is the locus of the moving point?
(A) an equilateral triangle
(B) a square
(C) a right triangle
(D) a circle

The area of a triangle having sides $\sqrt{3}$, $2\sqrt{2}$, and $\sqrt{11}$ is

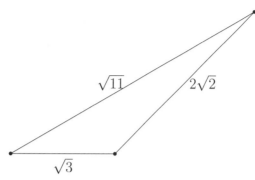

(Figure may not be drawn to scale.)

(A) $\sqrt{33}/2$ (B) $\sqrt{33}$ (C) $\sqrt{22}$ (D) $\sqrt{6}$

080. Similarity Ratio

A circle is inscribed in an equilateral triangle. A second equilateral triangle is inscribed in the circle. The ratio of the areas of the two triangles can be written as
(A) $1:4$
(B) $1:\sqrt{3}$
(C) $2:3$
(D) $5:7$

In the given figure, circle O has diameter $CD = 4$, $AC = 3$ and $\angle ACD \cong \angle BDC$. What is the measure of BC?

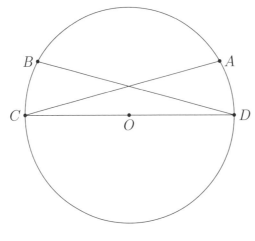

(A) 5   (B) $2\sqrt{2}$ (C) $\sqrt{7}$ (D) 3/2

Two circles have radii 3 and 6, respectively. If the line of the centers is 18, the length of the common internal tangent line is
(A) 9
(B) $6\sqrt{3}$
(C) $9\sqrt{3}$
(D) 12

083. Angle Chasing in Circle

In circle O, diameter $\overline{CD}$ bisects $\angle ACB$ where A and B are on O. If $m\angle ACD = 10°$, then arcACB must have the corresponding central angle measure of
(A) 20°
(B) 40°
(C) 60°
(D) 80°

084. Tangent Line / Secant Line

In the figure, $\overline{AB}$ is a tangent line to the circle and $\overline{AC}$ is a secant line through the center of the circle. If $AB = 2$ and external segment $\overline{AD}$ of the secant has the length of 1, what is the radius of the circle?

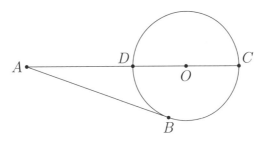

(A) 2/3   (B) 4/3   (C) 3/2   (D) 5/3

In $\triangle ABC$, as given in the figure, $AC = 5$ and $BC = 4$ where $\angle ACD \cong \angle BCD$, then the ratio of the area of $\triangle ACD$ to $\triangle DCB$ is

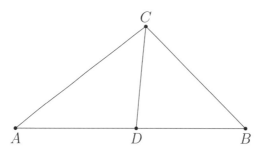

(A) $4:5$ (B) $5:4$ (C) $16:25$ (D) $25:16$

In the figure, $\overline{PA}$ is tangent to circle O. Chord $\overline{CD}$ is extended to E and $\overrightarrow{PA} \parallel \overrightarrow{CE}$. Based on the measures in the figure, the length of the radius equals

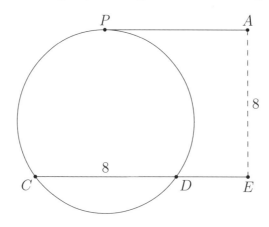

(A) 5 (B) $5\sqrt{3}$ (C) 6 (D) $6\sqrt{3}$

087. Definition of Angle Bisectors

Given two distinct rays, the angle bisector is the set of points equidistant from the two rays. If rays are extended enough to form two intersecting lines, which of the following best describes the locus of all points in the same plane equidistant from two intersecting lines?

(A) a ray that passes through the point of intersection.

(B) a circle centered at the point of intersection.

(C) the same two intersecting lines.

(D) two distinct intersecting lines, different from the original lines.

088. Isosceles Trapezoid

In the figure, $ABCD$ is a trapezoid with $AB = 15$, $CD = 9$, and $CB = AD = 5$. $\overline{CM}$ and $\overline{DN}$ are perpendicular to $\overline{AB}$ and $\overline{RS}$ is parallel to $\overline{DC}$. Then, MV equals

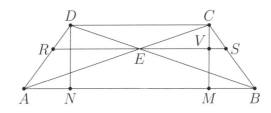

(A) 2   (B) 3   (C) 5/2   (D) 4

A circle of radius 1 is inscribed within a rhombus. A diagonal of the rhombus divides the quadrilateral into two equilateral triangles. Find the side length of the rhombus.

(A) $\dfrac{\sqrt{3}}{3}$ 　　　　(B) $\dfrac{2\sqrt{3}}{3}$ 　　　　(C) $\dfrac{4\sqrt{3}}{3}$ 　　　　(D) $\dfrac{4}{3}$

The largest possible area of a right triangle whose hypotenuse is 6 units in length is
(A) 9 square units
(B) $9\sqrt{2}$ square units
(C) $6\sqrt{2}$ square units
(D) $6\sqrt{3}$ square units

091. Angles in Circle - Sum / Difference

In the circle shown below, with center at O, $m\angle AEB = 15°$, and $m\angle COD = 8°$. Then, $m\angle CFD =$

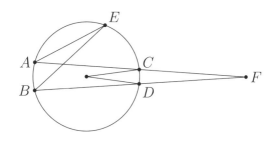

(A) 8°   (B) 11°   (C) 12°   (D) 15°

092. Variation of Midsegment Theorem in a Trapezoid

$ABCD$ is a trapezoid, with $\overline{AB}$ parallel to $\overline{CD}$. E and F are chosen on $\overline{AD}$ and $\overline{BC}$, respectively, so that $\dfrac{AE}{DE} = \dfrac{BF}{CF} = 2$. If $AB = 7$ and $CD = 10$, then find the length of EF.
(A) 7.5
(B) 8
(C) 8.5
(D) 9

A cylinder with the diameter of its base equal to its height is inscribed in a sphere of radius a. The ratio of the volume of the cylinder to the volume of the sphere can be written as $\frac{m\sqrt{n}}{p}$ where m, n and p are integers, and n is a square-free integer. If m and p are relatively prime positive integers, determine $m + n + p$.

(A) 11
(B) 12
(C) 13
(D) 14

If P is any point inside the equilateral triangle ABC and $AB = 6$, the sum of the perpendicular distances from P to each of the 3 sides is

(A) $3\sqrt{2}$
(B) $3\sqrt{3}$
(C) $4\sqrt{3}$
(D) $5\sqrt{3}$

095. Inradius / Incenter / Incircle

A circle is inscribed in a triangle with side lengths 6, 8, and 10. The area of the inscribed circle is

(A) π
(B) 2π
(C) 3π
(D) 4π

096. Circle Equations

The perimeter of the small arcs formed by intersecting the graphs of $x^2 + y^2 \leq 1$ and $(x-1)^2 + y^2 \leq 1$ must be equal to

(A) $\pi/2$
(B) $\pi/3$
(C) $4\pi/3$
(D) $3\pi/4$

097. Altitudes / Area of Triangle / Heron's Formula

The sides of a triangle are 5, 9, and 12. What is the length of the altitude to the side with length 12?

(A) $\dfrac{55}{12}$
(B) $\sqrt{\dfrac{55}{12}}$
(C) $\dfrac{104}{9}$
(D) $\sqrt{\dfrac{104}{9}}$

098. Circumdiameter and Hypotenuse

If a circle circumscribes a triangle with side length 5, 12, and 13, then the diameter of the circle must be
(A) 5
(B) 12
(C) 13
(D) 15

099. Circumcenter / Coordinate Geometry

$\triangle ABC$ has vertices $A(-2,3)$, $B(4,5)$ and $C(2,-3)$. The point of intersection of the perpendicular bisectors of all sides of $\triangle ABC$ is (x,y). The sum $x+y$ can be written in reduced fraction $\frac{m}{n}$ where m and n are relatively prime positive integers. Compute $m+n$.

(A) 44

(B) 45

(C) 46

(D) 47

100. Regular Polyhedron

Regular polyhedron is a 3-dimensional solid, all of whose faces consist of regular polygons. How many regular polyhedra are there?

(A) 3

(B) 5

(C) 7

(D) 9

101. Cyclic Quadrilateral

If a quadrilateral is inscribed in a circle, then
(A) consecutive angles are equal.
(B) consecutive angles are complementary.
(C) opposite angles are supplementary.
(D) it is necessarily a parallelogram.

102. Properties of Orthocenter

The intersection of the three altitudes of a triangle
(A) lies 2/3 of the way from any vertex to the opposite side.
(B) is the center of the inscribed circle.
(C) is not always unique.
(D) may be outside the triangle.

103. Area / Length / Angle Proportion in Circle

A circular segment is cut from a regular pentagon, with one vertex as center and a side of the pentagon as radius of the circle. If the area of this segment is 30π, the length of each side of the pentagon must be

(A) 10

(B) $30/\pi$

(C) $5\sqrt{6}$

(D) 3π

104. Regular Octagon

A regular octagon with the side length of $2\sqrt{2}$ has the area of $a + b\sqrt{c}$ where a, b, and c are integers such that c is square-free. Compute $a + b + c$.

(A) 32

(B) 34

(C) 36

(D) 38

105. Special Right Triangle

In a triangle ABC, if $m\angle A = 60°$ and $m\angle C = 90°$, and the median from C to $\overline{AB}$ has the length of 5, what is the length of $\overline{BC}$?
(A) 5
(B) $5\sqrt{3}$
(C) $5\sqrt{5}$
(D) $3\sqrt{5}$

106. Side-Angle Theorem / Angle Bisector Theorem

The sides of a triangle are 12, 18, and 20. The bisector of the greatest interior angle divides the opposite side into two segments of lengths
(A) 5 and 15
(B) 6 and 14
(C) 7.5 and 12.5
(D) 8 and 12

107. Definition of Parallelogram

Which one of the following statements is NOT correct?
(A) If two sides of a quadrilateral are parallel and equal, the figure is a parallelogram.
(B) If the diagonals of a quadrilateral bisect each other, the figure is a parallelogram.
(C) If two angles of a quadrilateral are supplementary, the figure is a parallelogram.
(D) If all two pairs of opposite sides of a given quadrilateral are parallel, the figure is a parallelogram.

108. Definition of Parallelogram

In parallelogram $ABCD$, P is the midpoint of $\overline{CD}$, M is the midpoint of $\overline{AP}$, T is the midpoint of $\overline{BP}$. $\overline{MT}$ is extended to meet $\overline{AD}$ at E and $\overline{BC}$ at F. If $AB = 12$, then $TF =$

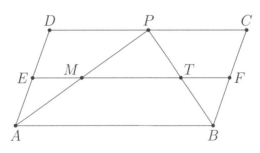

(A) $2\sqrt{2}$ (B) 3   (C) $2\sqrt{3}$ (D) 4

109. Five Centers in Circle Again - Part 1.

If there exists a point on a plane containing a triangle such that the distances from the point to each of the vertices are exactly equal to one another, the point can be found by drawing

(A) the medians of the triangle.

(B) the altitudes to triangular sides.

(C) the angle bisectors of interior angles of triangle

(D) the perpendicular bisectors of the sides of triangle

110. Five Centers in Circle Again - Part 2.

If there exists a point inside the triangle such that the distances from the point to each of the sides are exactly equal to one another, the point can be found by drawing

(A) the medians of the triangle.

(B) the altitudes to the sides.

(C) the interior angle bisectors.

(D) the bisectors of exterior angles.

The trapezoid $ABCD$ is inscribed about the circle with $AD = BC$. If $AB = 18$ and $DC = 16$, what is the radius of the circle?

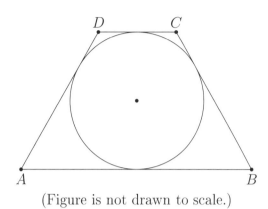

(Figure is not drawn to scale.)

(A) $3\sqrt{2}$ (B) $4\sqrt{3}$ (C) $6\sqrt{2}$ (D) $7\sqrt{2}$

112. Pythagoras Theorem or Heron's Formula

Given a triangle ABC such that $AB = 13$, $BC = 14$, and $AC = 15$, compute the area of the triangle.
(A) 80
(B) 82
(C) 84
(D) 86

113. Sum of Exterior Angles

The sum of the exterior angles of a convex polygon of six sides (angles formed by extending each side) is
(A) $360°$
(B) $480°$
(C) $720°$
(D) $900°$

114. Similar Figures

Given a rectangle $ABCD$, where $AB = CD$, $BC = AD = 3$ and $AB > BC$, if there exists a point E on $\overline{CD}$ such that $\overline{AE}$ is perpendicular to $\overline{BE}$ such that $DE = 2$, the area of $ABCD$ can be written as $\frac{m}{n}$ where m and n are relatively prime positive integers. Determine $m + n$.
(A) 39
(B) 41
(C) 43
(D) 45

Given an acute triangle ABC, there exists a circle such that it passes through B, tangent to $\overline{AC}$ at E. If $\overline{AB}$ and $\overline{BC}$ meet the circle at D and F, respectively, and $AD = CE = 4$ and $AE = BF = 6$. Compute the perimeter of $\triangle ABC$.

(A) 25

(B) 27

(C) 29

(D) 31

An equilateral triangle ABC is inscribed in a circle O, as shown in the figure below. If D is the midpoint of arc AB and if the radius of the circle is 5, then $CE =$

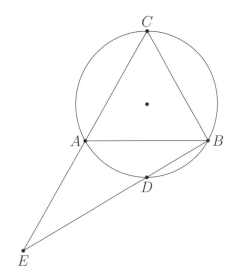

(A) 15   (B) $10\sqrt{3}$ (C) $15\sqrt{2}$ (D) $10\sqrt{2}$

Given the following statements :

(1) If I study hard, then I will get A on the geometry test.
(2) If I don't study hard, then I don't know geometry well.
(3) If I am accepted in one of the prestigious colleges, then I know geometry well.
(4) I did not make an A on the geometry test.

Which of the following conclusions is valid?
(A) I knew geometry well.
(B) I was accepted in college.
(C) I did not study hard, but I knew geometry well.
(D) I was not accepted in one of the prestigious colleges.

Two tangents to a circle form an angle of $72°$. If the radius of the circle is 10, then the length of the larger arc must be
(A) 12π
(B) 13π
(C) 14π
(D) 15π

119. Power of Points / Pythagorean Theorem

The radii of two concentric circles are 7 and 25. A chord of the larger circle is tangent to the smaller circle. The length of this chord is

(A) 32

(B) 40

(C) 48

(D) 49

120. Application of Angle Bisector Theorem

Given a triangle ABC, $\overline{BC}$ is extended and the bisector of the exterior angle at A meet at P. The length CP equals

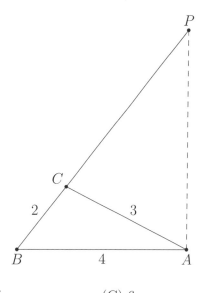

(A) 5   (B) 5.5   (C) 6   (D) 6.5

121. Sum of Exterior Angles of Regular Polygon

Each interior angle of a regular polygon is equal to 144°. How many sides does the polygon have?

(A) 6
(B) 8
(C) 10
(D) 12

122. Area of Equilateral Triangle

An equilateral triangle is inscribed in a circle of radius 2. The area inside the circle, but outside the triangle equals

(A) $4\pi - 3\sqrt{3}$
(B) $4\pi - 2\sqrt{3}$
(C) $4\pi - 2\sqrt{2}$
(D) $4\pi - 3\sqrt{2}$

123. Rhombus / Labeling

The longer diagonal of a rhombus is 16 and the perimeter is 40. The area of the rhombus must be equal to
(A) 96
(B) 120
(C) 128
(D) 144

124. Special Similar Figures

If the radius of a circle is doubled, the area of the resulting circle equals the original area multiplied by
(A) 2
(B) 3
(C) 4
(D) 5

125. Properties of Altitudes

If the lengths of the sides of a right triangle are 3, 4, and 5, what is the area of the smaller of the two triangles into which it is divided by a perpendicular from the vertex of the right angle to the hypotenuse?

(A) 9/4
(B) 54/25
(C) 12/5
(D) 45/16

126. Locus

The locus of the midpoints of all chords passing through point A on the given circle with center O is

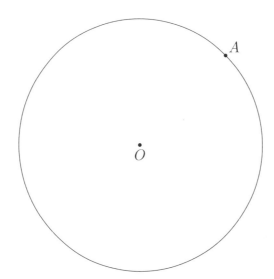

(A) an arc of a circle with center at A.
(B) a straight line segment.
(C) a circle with $\overline{OA}$ as diameter.
(D) two line segments with O as common endpoint.

127. The Importance of Setting-Up Variables

The length and width of a rectangle are in the ratio of 3 to 2. If its area equals 96, the perimeter is

(A) 36
(B) 40
(C) 44
(D) 48

128. Angle Bisector Theorem

The sides of a triangle are 12, 18, and 25. If the bisector of the greatest angle divides the opposite side, which of the following must be the difference of lengths of the newly formed sides?

(A) 3
(B) 4
(C) 5
(D) 6

If the diagonals of a rhombus has the length ratio of 2 to 3, and its side length equals 13, which of the following is equal to the area of the rhombus?
(A) 144
(B) 156
(C) 168
(D) 180

In a triangle ABC, if $m\angle A = 60°$ and $m\angle C = 90°$, and the median from C to $\overline{AB}$ has the length of 5, what is the length BC?
(A) $5\sqrt{3}$
(B) $3\sqrt{5}$
(C) $5\sqrt{5}$
(D) 5

131. Locus

What is the locus of the vertex of a triangle in a plane such that the triangle has a given area and a given line segment as its base?
(A) a circle with the base as its diameter.
(B) the circumcircle of the triangle.
(C) a circle with the vertex as center and radius length equal to the height of the triangle.
(D) two lines through the vertex and parallel to the base.

132. Trigonometry / Pythagorean Theorem

The number of degrees in two of the three interior angles of a triangle is 45. The ratio of the length of the longest side to the length of either of the other sides is
(A) $1 : 2$
(B) $2 : 1$
(C) $\sqrt{2} : 1$
(D) $1 : \sqrt{2}$

Which of the following is the correct expression for the base of a triangle whose area is $2x^2 + 5x - 3$ and whose height is $x + 3$?

(A) $4x - 1$

(B) $x - 1/2$

(C) $4x - 2$

(D) $2x - 1$

In circle O, $\overline{AB}$ is a chord perpendicular to the diameter $\overline{CD}$ at E. If $AB = 16$ and $CD = 34$, what is the length OE?

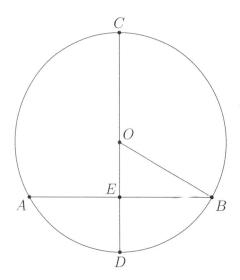

(A) $\sqrt{33}$ (B) 15   (C) 60   (D) 64

135. Parallelogram

The figure $ABCD$ is a parallelogram. If $AD = 3$, $AB = 5$, and $m\angle DAB = 30°$, then DB^2 can be written as $a - b\sqrt{c}$ where a, b, and c are positive integers, and c is a square-free integer. Compute $a + b + c$.

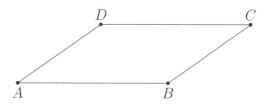

(A) 51
(B) 52
(C) 53
(D) 54

136. Inscribed Angle and Central Angle

In a circle that circumscribes $\triangle ABC$, if arc AB has the measure of $90°$, then $m\angle ACB =$

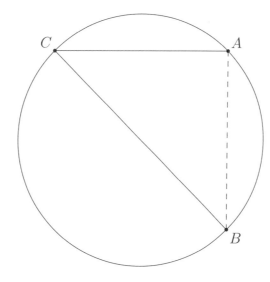

(A) 30°   (B) 45°   (C) 60°   (D) 90°

137. Angle Chasing in Circle

In a circle that circumscribes a quadrilateral $ABCD$, if arc AB has the measure of $90°$ and arc CD has the measure of $40°$, then $m\angle AEB =$

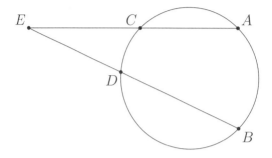

(A) $20°$
(B) $25°$
(C) $40°$
(D) $50°$

138. Application of Apothem

Given a regular hexagon, if the distance between the two parallel sides equals $4\sqrt{3}$, compute its side length.
(A) 2
(B) 3
(C) 4
(D) 5

Segments $\overline{AB}$ and $\overline{DE}$ are chords of a circle; the lines containing segments intersect in a point C which is *exterior* to the circle. If $AC = 4$, $BC = 5$, and $CD = 2$, then what is CE, assuming that the distance from E to C is longer than that from D to C?
(A) 4
(B) 6
(C) 8
(D) 10

Segments $\overline{AB}$ and $\overline{DE}$ are chords of a circle; the segments intersect in a point C which is *interior* to the circle. If $AC = 4$, $BC = 5$, and $CD = 2$, then what is CE?
(A) 4
(B) 6
(C) 8
(D) 10

141. Locus - Part 1.

Let A and B be distinct points in a plane. The locus of points P such that $PA = PB$ is contained in
(A) a straight line
(B) a single point
(C) a circle
(D) an ellipse

142. Locus - Part 2.

Let A and B be distinct points in a plane. The locus of points P such that $\angle APB$ is a right angle is
(A) a straight line
(B) a single point
(C) a circle
(D) an ellipse

In the figure, the segments $\overline{AA'}$, $\overline{BB'}$, and $\overline{CC'}$ are medians of the triangle ABC. If $AA' = 12$, $BB' = 11$ and $CC' = 10$, what is the length AO?

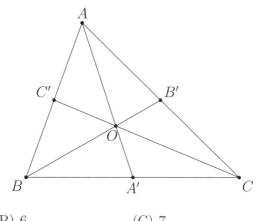

(A) 5   (B) 6   (C) 7   (D) 8

Given an acute triangle ABC, there exists F on $\overline{AB}$ and E on $\overline{BC}$ such that $\overline{AE}$ and $\overline{CF}$ meet at a point D inside the triangle ABC. If E is the midpoint of $\overline{BC}$ and $AF : BF = 2 : 1$, the ratio $\dfrac{AD}{DE}$ can be written as $\dfrac{m}{n}$. Determine $m + n$.

(A) 3
(B) 4
(C) 5
(D) 6

145. Counting in Geometry

How many quadrilaterals with vertices chosen from a regular decagon can be formed in total?
(A) 150
(B) 180
(C) 210
(D) 240

146. Properties of Cyclic Quadrilateral

If the vertices of a quadrilateral lie on a circle, the perpendicular bisectors of all the sides
(A) intersect at a point.
(B) are equal.
(C) are perpendicular to each other.
(D) bisect the opposite sides also.

147. Special Right Triangle / Labeling and Setting-up Equations

If the area of an equilateral triangle with altitude of length 12 can be written as $a\sqrt{b}$ where b is a square-free integer, compute $a + b$.

(A) 48
(B) 51
(C) 54
(D) 57

148. Pythagorean Theorem / Power of Points

A circle centered at O has a chord $\overline{XY}$ of length 16, which is 12 units away from the center. If the area of circle can be written as $k\pi$ where k is an integer, compute the value of k.

(A) 204
(B) 206
(C) 208
(D) 210

149. Properties of Median

Let ABC be a triangle such that $\overline{AP}$ and $\overline{BQ}$ are congruent medians, where $AP = BQ = 6$. If $\overline{AP} \perp \overline{BQ}$, then the area of ABC is equal to
(A) 12
(B) 16
(C) 20
(D) 24

150. Properties of Orthocenter

Let ABC be a triangle such that $AB = 13$, $BC = 14$ and $AC = 15$. If there exists a circle ω_1 on the same plane such that its diameter equals $\overline{AB}$ and another circle ω_2 whose diameter equals $\overline{AC}$, both circles meet at two distinct points. Compute the distance between the two points.
(A) 9
(B) 12
(C) 15
(D) 18

Part 2

Solution Manual

for 150 Problems

001. The answer is (B). A plane is a geometric object that can be thought of as an infinitely large, flat surface that extends indefinitely in all directions without any edges or boundaries. It is a two-dimensional object, which means it has only length and width but no thickness. It is also a mathematical concept that can be described using equations and coordinates.

002. The answer is (D). Three non-collinear points, also known as three points that are not on the same line, are used to define a unique plane in geometry. This is because a plane is defined as the set of all points that are equidistant from the three given points. The three points determine the position of the plane in space and the distance between the plane and each of the points.

However, if the three points are collinear, they do not form a unique plane. This is because collinear points lie on the same line and there are infinitely many planes that pass through a line. Imagine a piece of paper that is rotating along the line in its middle. The paper can rotate to any angle, and in each angle, it forms a different plane that passes through the line of the three collinear points.

In other words, if the three points are collinear, they don't define a unique plane because any plane that goes through the line determined by these points will pass through these three points. In contrast, if three non-collinear points are given, there is only one plane that passes through these three points.

003. The answer is (C). There are four distinct points in the figure. Choose the first point out of the four points. Then, choose the second point out of the three remaining points. Hence, there are 4×3 pairs. However, the segment can be labeled in reverse order, so we must get rid of the overcounts. Thus, the answer must be 6.

004. The answer is (C). Fix a vertex, let's say A. Then, connect it with adjacent vertices to find out there are three types of segments that can be drawn from A. The first must be the segment congruent to the side of regular hexagon. The second must be the segment congruent to shorter diagonal of the regular hexagon. The last must be the segment congruent to the longest diagonal of the figure.

005. The answer is (D). From the given condition, we set $AB = CD$. Hence, $2x - 1 = 3x - 4$ implies that $x = 3$. This means that $AB = CD = 5$. Since $AB + CD = 5 + 5$, by substitution, we conclude that $AB + CD = 10$.

006. The answer is (D). Let $AB = CD$, according to the given condition. Then, $3 - 2x = 3x - 7$ implies that $x = 2$. However, the segment has its length at least 0. if $x = 2$, $AB = CD = -1$, which contradicts the assumption that any segment has non-negative length. Therefore, there is no such x value satisfying the given condition.

007. The answer is (B). Let x be the coordinate of C. Then, $AC = x - 5$ and $CB = 10 - x$, according to the definition of absolute value on a real number line. Hence, $x - 5 : 10 - x = 2 : 3$ implies that $20 - 2x = 3x - 15$. Therefore, $5x = 35$, implying that $x = 7$. Since $5 < 7 < 10$, the coordinate of C must be 7.

008. The answer is (D). Let c be the coordinate of C. First, assume that C is between A and B. Then, $AC : CB = 2 : 3$ implies that $c - 2 : 12 - c = 2 : 3$. Hence, $c = 6$. Second, assume that C is not between A and B. Then, $AC : CB = 2 : 3$ implies that $2 - c : 12 - c = 2 : 3$. Hence, $c = -18$. The sum of all possible coordinates of c is -12. Such coordinates we found are known as the intersection points between the line containing A and B and the circle of Apollonius. Another way to solve this problem is to translate $(A, B) = (2, 10)$ into $(A', B') = (0, 10)$ such that the interior point turns out to be 4 and the exterior point -20. We may translate the points 2 units right again to conclude that c is either 6 or -18.

009. The answer is (D). Draw auxiliary lines — vertical and horizontal lines — at the three given points. Then, the resulting figure has a rectangle of area 8. Get rid of three right triangles of area 2, 1, and 2. Hence, the area of triangle formed by the three points must be 3. Similar to question 27 and 28, one may use Shoelace Theorem to compute the area of the triangle.

The shoelace theorem, also known as the Gauss area formula, is a mathematical result that can be used to determine the area of a simple polygon. A simple polygon is a polygon with no self-intersections, which means the sides do not cross over each other.

The shoelace theorem states that the area of a simple polygon can be calculated by taking the sum of the product of the x-coordinates of the vertices and the y-coordinates of the vertices that follow them, and subtracting the sum of the product of the y-coordinates of the vertices and the x-coordinates of the vertices that follow them. This is how we use Shoelace Theorem. Given the coordinates $(1, 1)$, $(3, 3)$ and $(2, 5)$, we get $\frac{1}{2} \times |(1 \cdot 3 + 3 \cdot 5 + 2 \cdot 1) - (1 \cdot 3 + 3 \cdot 2 + 5 \cdot 1)| = \frac{1}{2} \times |20 - 14| = 3$.

The shoelace theorem can also be extended to calculate the centroid of a polygon. A centroid is the geometric center of a polygon, and it can be represented as (C_x, C_y). The centroid of a polygon can be found by taking the average of x-coordinates and y-coordinates of the vertices of the polygon. It is important to note that the shoelace theorem is only applicable for simple polygon, if the polygon is self-intersecting or concave, the shoelace theorem will not work.

010. The answer is (A). We apply the equivalent strategies as in the previous question. The resulting figure has a rectangle of area 20. Get rid of four right triangles of area 2, 1.5, 3, and 3. Hence, the area of quadrilateral formed by the four points must be 10.5.

011. The answer is (A). The difference in x-values is 3 and that in y-values is 4. Thus, the distance between the two points equals $\sqrt{3^2 + 4^2} = \sqrt{25} = 5$.

012. The answer is (B). According to the taxicab metric, the distance between A and B can be computed as the sum of the difference in x-values and that in y-values, which equals 7. In other words, the horizontal translation of 4 units and the vertical translation of 3 units are combined as 7 units of movement.

013. The answer is (C). Imagine a right triangle that stands in a space. The bottom side has the length of $\sqrt{1^2 + 1^2} = \sqrt{2}$. Since the height of the triangle equals 2, we may use the pythagorean theorem such that

$$OA = \sqrt{(\sqrt{2})^2 + 2^2} = \sqrt{2 + 4} = \sqrt{6}.$$

014. The answer is (B). Along with the previous question, we may conclude that the distance formula can be extended to space points, i.e.,

$$\sqrt{(3-1)^2 + (4-2)^2 + (6-3)^2} = \sqrt{4 + 4 + 9} = \sqrt{17}$$

015. The answer is (C). Two angles are complementary if and only if the sum of their measures equals $90°$. Hence,

$$m\angle A + m\angle B = 30° - x + 45° + 2x = 75° + x = 90°$$

Thus, $x = 15°$.

016. The answer is (D). The set of points equidistant from two intersecting lines in a plane is known as the angle bisector line of the angles formed by the two lines. This is because the angle bisector line divides the angle formed by the two lines into two congruent angles.

The vertical angle congruence postulate states that if two lines intersect, then the opposite angles formed are congruent, or equal in measure. This means that if two lines intersect, they form two pairs of congruent angles. One pair of these angles is formed by the angle bisectors of the two lines. Since these angle bisectors divide the angles formed by the two lines into congruent angles, they are also congruent.

As a result, there are two "perpendicular" lines formed by the angle bisectors of the two intersecting lines. These perpendicular lines are called angle bisectors. The two angle bisectors are perpendicular to each other because they are formed by the intersection of two lines that form a right angle at the point of intersection, due to the vertical angle congruence postulate.

017. The answer is (A). If three distinct planes in space are to intersect, there are two possibilities for the shape of their intersection: a straight line or a single point.

The first possibility is that the three planes have a common line among themselves. This means that all three planes intersect at a single straight line, which is the intersection of the three planes. This line is also known as the line of intersection of the three planes. The line of intersection is the set of all points that are common to all three planes.

The second possibility is that the three planes meet up at a single point. This means that the three planes intersect at a single point, which is the intersection of the three planes. This point is also known as the point of intersection of the three planes. The point of intersection is the set of all points that are common to all three planes. To illustrate this, imagine a typical xyz-plane. The origin $O(0,0,0)$ is the common point of intersection of the x, y, and z-plane. This point is the point of intersection of the three planes because it is a point that belongs to all three planes.

018. The answer is (B). The statement that "two distinct points always form a unique line passing through the two" is known as the first postulate of Euclidean geometry, which states that any two distinct points in space can be connected by a straight line, and that this line is unique. Similarly, the statement that "given any line, one may always find two distinct points that would have resulted in graphing that line" is known as the second postulate of Euclidean geometry. This postulate states that for any given line, there are always two distinct points that can be used to define it.

The statement "three non-collinear points form a unique plane" is also a fundamental postulate of Euclidean geometry. This postulate states that any three non-collinear points in space can be used to define a unique plane. Likewise, given any plane, one may spot three non-collinear points that would have formed it. This means that for any given plane, there are always three non-collinear points that can be used to define it.

019.

(a) It is true. Non-adjacent angles can be complementary as long as the sum of their measures equal to $90°$.

(b) It is true. This is a definition of linear pair. Linear pair implies that the angles in such pair are adjacent and supplementary at the same time.

(c) It is false. Three collinear points never form a unique plane. Also, there is no phrase about three distinct points. One may argue that three indistinct points do not determine a unique plane.

(d) It is false. Some two non-parallel lines in space are skew, never meeting at a point.

(e) It is true. Two distinct planes that are not parallel to one another will eventually meet at a line.

(f) It is false. There exists only one line passing through two distinct points. Since there is at least one counter-example to the given statement, it is false.

020.

(a) It is false. Consider $x = -\sqrt{3}$, which satisfies the hypothesis, but not the conclusion.

(b) It is false. Any real number has its square greater than or equal to 0. Hence, the hypothesis is always satisfied, yet the conclusion will always stay false.

(c) It is true. At $x = 1$, both hypothesis and conclusion are true. Mathematical statement is true if both are true. One may refer to the Law of Detachment.

(d) It is true. This is a contrapositive statement of (c). Since the truth value for the original statement and its contrapositive do not change, we may safely conclude that this is true.

(e) It is false. There are two values $x = \pm 1$ satisfying the hypothesis, but there is only one value in the conclusion. Hence, the hypothesis is satisfied at $x = -1$, but the conclusion is false. Hence, $x = -1$ is the counterexample to the given statement.

(f) It is false because this is a contrapositive of (e).

021. The answer is (B). According to the segment additional postulate, $AB + BC = AC$, since A, B, and C are collinear.

022. The answer is (C). According to triangular inequality, $AC + BC > AB$. If A, C, and B are collinear, then $AC + BC = AB$. However, since C is not on the line containing A and B, then a triangle ABC must be formed to satisfy triangular inequality.

023. The answer is (B). Let the coordinate of B be k. Then, $AB = k - 3$ and $BC = 10 - k$. Hence, $AB : BC = k - 3 : 10 - k = 4 : 7$ implies that $k = \dfrac{61}{11}$. Hence, $m + n = 61 + 11 = 72$.

024. The answer is (C). Since $2(2x - 10) = 3x + 1$, we get $x = 21$. Thus, $m\angle DAC = (2(21) - 10)^\circ = 32^\circ$.

025. The answer is (C). The line containing $(3, 4)$ that is perpendicular to $y = x$ has the equation $x + y = 7$. Hence, the intersection point between $y = x$ and $x + y = 7$ is $(3.5, 3.5)$. The distance between $(3, 4)$ and $(3.5, 3.5)$ equals $\sqrt{(0.5)^2 + (0.5)^2} = \sqrt{0.5} = \sqrt{2}/2$.

Here is another way to solve this problem. Let t be the distance from $(3, 4)$ to $y = x$. Then, we use similar triangles to set up a ratio expression.

$$t : 1 = 3 : 3\sqrt{2}$$
$$3 = 3\sqrt{2}t$$
$$t = \frac{1}{\sqrt{2}}$$

026. The answer is (D). Using the coordinate geometry, we find out the vertical distance between the lines is 4 and the horizontal distance is 2. Hence, we are simply looking for the height to the hyptoneuse of a right triangle whose lengths are 2 and 4. Let such height be d. Then, $d = \frac{4}{\sqrt{5}}$, since the length of its hypotenuse is $2\sqrt{5}$, and its area is 4. Since $\frac{m}{n} = d^2 = \frac{16}{5}$, where 16 and 5 are relatively prime positive integers, the sum of m and n is 21.

027. The answer is (B). The base length must be 2, whereas the height must be 2. The area of a newly formed triangle is $\frac{1}{2} \times 2 \times 2 = 2$.

028. The answer is (C). According to shoelace theorem, the parallelogram formed by A, B, and C has the area of 9. Therefore, the triangle area must be $\frac{9}{2}$.

029. The answer is (A). Let $k - d$, k, and $k + d$ be the measures of interior angles. Then, $k = 60°$. Hence, $0 < 60 - d$ and $60 + d < 180$. Hence, $d < 60$. Since d must be integer, $d = 1, 2, 3, \cdots, 59$.

030. The answer is (A). According to the exterior angle theorem, the sum of measures of two remote angles equals the measure of exterior angle. Hence,
$41 - 2x + 2x + 43 = 84$.

031. The answer is (A). The circumcenter of a triangle is a point that is equidistant from all three vertices of the triangle. It is the center of the circle that passes through all three vertices of the triangle, which is called the circumcircle.

032. The answer is (B). The incenter of a triangle is a point that is equidistant from the three sides of the triangle. It is the center of the circle inscribed in the triangle, which is a circle that is tangent to all three sides of the triangle at their points of concurrency. One way to find the incenter of a triangle is by looking for the point of concurrency among the angle bisectors of the triangle's interior angles. An angle bisector is a line that divides an angle into two congruent angles. By drawing the angle bisectors of all three interior angles of the triangle, we can find the point where they intersect, which is the incenter of the triangle.

033. The answer is (A). Consider SSA ambiguous case. The answer choice (A) may produce SSA ambiguous case.

034. The answer is (B). The sum of exterior angles of the figure in the question, in fact, all planar convex polygons, must be 360°.

035. The answer is (D). Similar figures have a fixed ratio of sides and congruent corresponding angles. Hence, the fixed ratio is not necessarily 1.

036. The answer is (B). Since tangents are congruent to one another, $3x - 1 = 5$ implies that $x = 2$.

037. The answer is (C). Equilateral triangles can be expressed as isosceles triangles whose vertex angle measure equals 60°. All equilateral triangles are similar but not always congruent, though it might not be necessarily referenced.

038. The answer is (C). If lines are parallel, then we may use alternate interior angle theorem(or postulate) such that any alternate interior angle pair consists of congruent angles. The alternate interior angle theorem states that if two lines are parallel, then any pair of alternate interior angles are congruent, or equal in measure. Alternate interior angles are angles that are on opposite sides of a transversal line and are between the two parallel lines.

This theorem is based on the fact that when two lines are parallel, the alternate interior angles are formed by the intersection of the transversal line with the two parallel lines. These angles are congruent because they are formed by the intersection of the same transversal line with the two parallel lines.

039. The answer is (C). The volume of a sphere must be $\frac{4}{3}\pi r^3$.

040. The answer is (B). The sum of radii equals the distance between the centers. Hence, there is only one point of intersection between the two circles.

041. The answer is (C). It is obvious that $AB < AC$ and $BC < AC$ because of side-angle theorem. Larger interior angle produces larger opposite side length.

042. The answer is (B). Using Pythagorean Theorem, we may find that $PQ = 2\sqrt{10}$. Due to congruent tangents, we get $PS = SR = SQ = \sqrt{10}$.

043. The answer is (B). In an isosceles triangle, angle bisectors of the base angles are congruent due to ASA congruence postulate and CPCTC, which stands for "Corresponding Parts of Congruent Triangles are Congruent." This is a theorem in Euclidean geometry that states that if two triangles are congruent, then all corresponding parts of the two triangles are also congruent.

Likewise, the ASA (Angle-Side-Angle) postulate is a statement in Euclidean geometry that states that if in two triangles, two angles and the included side of one triangle are congruent to two corresponding angles and the included side of another triangle, then the two triangles are congruent.

044. The answer is (C). Since a regular pentagon can be formed by connecting three triangles, the sum of interior angle measures must be 540°.

045. The answer is (D). Triangle ABC and MBN are similar due to SAS similarity. Hence, $MN : BC = 1 : 2$. Since $BC = 8$, we conclude that $MN = 4$.

046. The answer is (B). The set of vertices whose base equals $\overline{AB}$ must stay on the perpendicular bisector of $\overline{AB}$. Since perpendicular bisector is a line, the answer must be (B).

047. The answer is (D). Diagonals of a quadrilateral are bisected if and only if the polygon is a parallelogram. A parallelogram is a quadrilateral that has opposite sides parallel and congruent, and opposite angles are congruent. When the diagonals of a parallelogram are drawn, they bisect each other at their midpoint. This is because the diagonals of a parallelogram are both medians and altitudes of the quadrilateral, and medians and altitudes of any shape bisect each other.

048. The answer is (B). The measure of segment $\overline{AB}$ can be at most the diameter of a circle. Hence, the chord length must be smaller than or equal to the diameter length.

049. The answer is (D). Given a chord connecting two points on the circle, its perpendicular bisector always passes through the center, containing the diameter.

050. The answer is (D). If folded into half along the line of symmetry, the figure must be completely overlapped. Hence, there are four such lines passing through the center.

051. The answer is (C). The sum of exterior angles of dodecagon must be $360°$.

052. The answer is (C). Altitude from B has its base $\overline{AC}$. Since $\angle C$ is right, the altitude is congruent to $\overline{BC}$.

053. The answer is (A). Since $2\pi r = 4$, we get $r = \frac{2}{\pi}$. Thus, the area of triangle must be $\pi r^2 = \frac{4}{\pi}$, which is closest to 1.

054. The answer is (C). A parallelepiped is a 3-dimensional geometric shape with six rectangular faces that are parallelograms. It is a rectangular prism with parallelogram faces. It is a polyhedron that has six faces that are parallelograms, and opposite faces are congruent. Special kind of parallelepiped is a prism, hence, prism and parallelepiped are equivalent kinds.

055. The answer is (D). Given a right triangle, its hypotenuse is always equal to its circumdiameter. Hence, we are looking for the circumcenter of the right triangle. Hence, it must be the midpoint of the hypotenuse, which can easily be found by the point of concurrency among perpendicular bisectors of all sides.

056. The answer is (B). The only answer choice that may have been true is (C), but if two lines are skew, then they are not parallel.

057. The answer is (C). This is simply the definition of contrapositive of the original mathematical statement.

058. The answer is (B). The base area must be $\sqrt{3}$, and it height must be $\frac{\sqrt{8}}{\sqrt{3}}$, which can be found by applying Pythagorean Theorem. Hence, the volume must be $\frac{1}{3} \times \sqrt{3} \times \frac{\sqrt{8}}{\sqrt{3}} = \frac{2\sqrt{2}}{3}$. Hence, $a + b + c = 2 + 2 + 3 = 7$.

059. The answer is (C). When we say that two planes are distinct, it means that they are not the same plane. They do not share the same set of points and do not have the same orientation in space. In other words, they are different planes that do not overlap. If we have two distinct planes, we can be sure that they cannot be identical. This is because planes that are identical would have to share the same set of points and have the same orientation in space, which is not possible for two distinct planes.

060. The answer is (C). The ratio between the inscribed angle measure and the central angle measure is 1 to 2. Hence, the ratio we want must be $\frac{2}{1} = 2$.

061. The answer is (B). If we let $AE = k$, then $k^2 + 4^2 = 5^2$ implies that $k = 3$. Hence, the lengths of bases are 19 and 10, and the height is 4. Thus, the area of trapezoid must be $\frac{1}{2} \times 4 \times (10 + 19) = 58$.

062. The answer is (C). Given a fixed point, there exists a sphere equidistant from the point. Imagine this sphere rotating around the given line as its axis of movement. Its trace must result in a cylinder-shaped figure that does not end.

063. The answer is (D). Since $OB = 12$, and $m\angle ABC = 120°$, we can conclude that $m\angle AOC = 60°$. By HL congruence, we get $m\angle AOB = m\angle COB = 30°$. Hence, $AO = OC = 6\sqrt{3}$, and $AB = BC = 6$.

064. The answer is (B). All squares are similar to one another. Since $BD : CD = \sqrt{2} : 1$, the area ratio must be $2 : 1$. Thus, the area of $BDEF$ must be twice that of $ABCD$, which means that the area of $BDEF$ is 6.

065. The answer is (C). According to similarities, $18 : MB = MB : 8$, so $MB^2 = 8 \times 18 = 12^2 = 144$. Hence, $MB = 12$.

066. The answer is (A). The shorter diagonal can be bisected into the segments of length 6. According to special right triangle property, we get the longer diagonal having the length of $12\sqrt{3}$. Thus, the side measure of the rhombus is 12.

067. The answer is (C). When we negate the hypothesis and the conclusion of a statement, we obtain a new statement that is called the inverse of the original statement. The inverse of a statement is formed by reversing the direction of the logical relationship between the hypothesis and the conclusion.

068. The answer is (D). Since X is the midpoint of $\overline{AB}$, we get $AX = BX$ and X between A and B.

069. The answer is (C). Given four different lines, we must choose two lines to form a unique plane. Hence, there are $\binom{4}{2} = \frac{4 \times 3}{2} = 6$ different planes formed by the lines.

070. The answer is (A). According to the special right triangle property, we use $1 : \sqrt{3} : 2$ to solve for the problem. Let k be the length of the shortest leg. Then, the other two lengths must be $k\sqrt{3}$ and $2k$. Since $2k = 10$, we get $k = 5$. There are two possible values of legs, i.e., 5 and $5\sqrt{3}$. Out of answer choices, (A) is the only answer choice that has one of the two values.

071. The answer is (D). Since the circumdiameter becomes the hypotenuse for the right isosceles triangle, we get the side length of the square as $2\sqrt{2}$. Thus, its area must be $(2\sqrt{2})^2 = 8$.

072. The answer is (D). Out of all answer choices, $QM : QF = \sqrt{3} : 2$, according to the special right triangle property. Hence, $QM^2 : QF^2 = 3 : 4$. Thus, (D) must be correct.

073. The answer is (D). When a line is given in space, we can draw a line that is perpendicular to it by finding a point on the given line and then drawing a line that is perpendicular to the given line and passing through that point. This can be done in infinitely many ways, by choosing different points on the given line, we can draw infinitely many lines that are perpendicular to it.

074. The answer is (C). First, the midpoint of -7 and 3 must be -2. Second, the midpoint of 6 and -4 is 1. Hence, the midpoint must be $(-2, 1)$.

075. The answer is (D). This is a basic application of midsegment theorem which states that in a triangle, the segment that connects the midpoints of two sides is parallel to the third side and is half the length of that side. In other words, in a triangle, the midsegment is parallel to the third side and its length is half the length of the third side. Hence, $\overline{DF}$ is parallel to $\overline{BC}$ and $DF : BC = 1 : 2$, due to SAS similarity.

076. The answer is (D). All answer choices except (D) are true due to similar triangles. However, $KP^2 \neq QK^2 + QP^2$.

077. The answer is (B). According to the power of point theorem, we get $AS \cdot SB = CS \cdot SD$. Hence, $2 \times 3 = k \times 4$. Therefore, $k = \frac{3}{2}$.

078. The answer is (D). Given perpendicular lines, label the lines as x-axis and y-axis. Then, the sum of the squares of the point's distances from the two axes can be identified as $x^2 + y^2$, if the point has the coordinates of (x, y). Hence, the locus must be a circle.

079. The answer is (D). Drop the perpendicular foot from the vertex opposite the longest side. Let its height be b, and the longest side be cut into segments of length a and $\sqrt{11} - a$. Hence, $a^2 + b^2 = 3$ and $(\sqrt{11} - a)^2 + b^2 = 8$. Then, $a = \frac{3}{\sqrt{11}}$. Thus, $b^2 = \frac{24}{11}$. Thus, the area must be $\frac{2\sqrt{6}}{2} = \sqrt{6}$.

080. The answer is (A). All equilateral triangles are similar to one another, so if we get the length ratio, we can easily get the area ratio. Since the side length of the larger triangle is twice that of the smaller triangle, we get the area ratio of $1:4$ or $4:1$. The only answer choice that matches with this conclusion is (A).

081. The answer is (C). Since $\triangle ACD \cong \triangle BDC$, we get $AD = BC = \sqrt{16-9} = \sqrt{7}$.

082. The answer is (C). This is a typical application of Pythagorean Theorem. The common internal tangent can be found by a right triangle whose hypotenuse has the length of 18 and height has the length of 9. Thus, the common internal tangent must have the length of $9\sqrt{3}$.

083. The answer is (B). An inscribed angle is an angle formed by two chords of a circle that share an endpoint on the circle. The central angle of a circle is an angle formed by two radii of the circle that share an endpoint on the circle. The ratio of inscribed angle measure and central angle measure is 1 to 2 means that for any inscribed angle in a circle, the measure of the inscribed angle is half the measure of the central angle that intercepts the same arc. Since the inscribed angle measure equals $20°$, we get the central angle measure of $40°$.

084. The answer is (C). According to the power of point, we get $AB^2 = AD \cdot AC = 1 \cdot (1+2r) = 4$. Thence, $1 + 2r = 4$. Thus, $2r = 3$. Therefore, $r = \frac{3}{2}$.

085. The answer is (B). According to the angle bisector theorem, we get $AC : BC = AD : BD$. Let $AD = 5k$, $BD = 4k$, and h be the height from C to $\overline{AB}$. Thus, $[ACD] : [BCD] = \frac{5kh}{2} : 2kh$. Thus, $[ACD] : [BCD] = 5 : 4$.

086. The answer is (A). The chord is perpendicularly bisected by the diameter, which can be labeled as $8 + x$, where 8 is the length of AE and x is that of the remaining part of the diameter. Hence, according to the power of point theorem, we get $8x = 16$. Thus, $x = 2$. Since the diameter has the length of 10, the radius has the length of 5.

087. The answer is (D). The locus of two intersecting lines in a plane that satisfy the given condition must be two perpendicular lines, different from the original lines.

088. The answer is (C). According to the property of isosceles trapezoid, $CV : MV = 3 : 5$. Since $CM = 4$, we get $CV + MV = 3k + 5k = 4$. Thus, $k = \frac{1}{2}$, implying that $MV = \frac{5}{2}$.

089. The answer is (C). Using the similar triangles inside the right triangle, let $2k$ be the length of its hypotenuse. Then, k and $k\sqrt{3}$ are its side lengths. Hence, $\frac{1}{2} \times k \times k\sqrt{3} = \frac{1}{2} \times 2k \times 1$. Thus, $k = \frac{2\sqrt{3}}{3}$. Therefore, $2k = \frac{4\sqrt{3}}{3}$.

090. The answer is (A). Recall that the hypotenuse of a right triangle equals the circumdiameter of its circumcircle. The largest height can be the length of its radius. Thus, $\frac{1}{2} \times 6 \times 3 = 9$.

091. The answer is (B). Length chasing tells us that the central angle measure of AB is $30°$ and that of CD is $8°$. Hence, $m\angle CFD = \frac{30° - 8°}{2} = \frac{22°}{2} = 11°$.

092. The answer is (D). This is an application of midsegment theorem. $EF : \frac{27}{2} = 2 : 3$. Hence, $EF = 9$.

093. The answer is (C). The volume of a sphere must be $\frac{4\pi a^3}{3}$ and the volume of cylinder must be $\pi(\frac{\sqrt{2}a}{2})^2 \times \sqrt{2}a = \frac{2\sqrt{2}\pi a^3}{4}$. Hence, the volume ratio of cylinder to sphere must be $\frac{6\sqrt{2}}{18} = \frac{3\sqrt{2}}{8}$. Hence, $m + n + p = 13$.

094. The answer is (B). Let distances from P to all sides as x, y and z. Then, the area of the triangle can be written as $3(x + y + z)$. On the other hand, the area of equilateral triangle must be $\frac{\sqrt{3}}{4} \times 6^2 = 9\sqrt{3}$. Thus, $x + y + z = 3\sqrt{3}$.

095. The answer is (D). First, we chase lengths to find out the inradius of length 2. Or, we may have used the area method such that we cut the triangle into three triangles such that $12r = \frac{1}{2} \times 6 \times 8$. Either way, we get $r = 2$.

096. The answer is (C). Intersecting part forms two arcs whose central angle measure equals $120°$. Since the radii are 1 for both circles, we get $2\pi(1) \times \frac{120°}{360°} \times 2 = \frac{4\pi}{3}$.

097. The answer is (D). Label the height as k. This altitude will cut the base into two segments of length x and $12 - x$, where the segment of length x is closer to the side of length 9. Then, $x^2 + k^2 = 81$ and $(12 - x)^2 + k^2 = 25$. Hence, $x = \frac{25}{3}$. Thus, $k^2 = 9^2 - (\frac{25}{3})^2 = \frac{104}{9}$. Therefore, $k = \sqrt{\frac{104}{9}}$.

098. The answer is (C). Given a triangle with side lengths 5, 12, and 13, its circumdiameter equals its hypotenuse., since it is a right triangle.

099. The answer is (C). The perpendicular bisector of $\overline{AC}$ can be written as $y = \frac{2}{3}x$. The perpendicular bisector of $\overline{AB}$ can be written as $y = -3(x - 1) + 4 = -3x + 7$. Since $\frac{2}{3} = \frac{y}{x}$, let $y = 2k$ and $x = 3k$. Thus, $2k = -9k + 7$. Therefore, $k = \frac{7}{11}$. Hence, $x + y = 5k = \frac{35}{11}$. The sum of numerator and denominator in reduced form must be 46.

Here is another way to solve it. We may set up $AP^2 = BP^2 = CP^2$ for $P(x, y)$. Then, $(x + 2)^2 + (y - 3)^2 = (x - 4)^2 + (y - 5)^2 = (x - 2)^2 + (y + 3)^2$ implies that $4x - 6y + 13 = -4x + 6y + 13 = -8x - 10y + 41$. Thus, $2x = 3y$, $11y = 14$, so $x + y = \frac{5}{2}y = \frac{5}{2} \times \frac{14}{11} = \frac{35}{11}$.

100. The answer is (B). There are five regular polyhedra − tetrahedron, hexahedron, octahedron, dodecahedron, and icosahedron.

101. The answer is (C). A cyclic quadrilateral is a quadrilateral in which all four vertices lie on a single circle. A quadrilateral is cyclic if and only if the opposite angles are supplementary, meaning they add up to 180 degrees. The second property of a cyclic quadrilateral is that congruent inscribed angles produce similar triangles within the quadrilateral. An inscribed angle is an angle formed by two chords of a circle that share an endpoint on the circle. When two inscribed angles in a cyclic quadrilateral are congruent, the triangles formed by the inscribed angles and the chord of the angle are similar.

102. The answer is (D). Orthocenter may stay within the figure or outside the figure. Similarly, the circumcenter may stay within or outside the figure. However, the centroid or incenter must stay inside the figure.

103. The answer is (A). The sector area can be written as $\pi r^2 \times \frac{108°}{360°} = 30\pi$. Hence, $r = 10$. Since r refers to the side length of the pentagon, we conclude that the side length must be 10.

104. The answer is (B). Imagine cutting four right isosceles triangles from a square whose side length must be $4 + 2\sqrt{2}$. Hence, $(4 + 2\sqrt{2})^2 - 4 \times (\frac{1}{2} \times 2 \times 2) = 16 + 16\sqrt{2} + 8 - 8 = 16 + 16\sqrt{2}$. The answer must be 34.

105. The answer is (B). Using special right triangle property, we get $AC = 5$, $BC = 5\sqrt{3}$ and $AB = 10$ because the median from C to $\overline{AB}$ is circumradius of $\triangle ABC$.

106. The answer is (D). The angle bisector cuts the longest side into segments with the ratio of 12 to 18. Label the shorter one as $12k$ and the longer one as $18k$. The sum must be $30k = 20$. Hence, $k = \frac{2}{3}$. Thus, $12k = 8$ and $18k = 12$. The two segments have the lengths of 8 and 12.

107. The answer is (C). If the supplementary angles are non-adjacent, then the figure is cyclic, but not necessarily a parallelogram.

108. The answer is (B). If $AB = 12$, then $MT = 6$. Since P is the midpoint of $\overline{CD}$, we get $PD = CP = 6$. Thus, $TF = EM = 3$, by similar figures of length ratio of 1 to 2.

109. The answer is (D). This is a definition of circumcenter.

110. The answer is (C). This is a definition of incenter.

111. The answer is (C). Let r be the radius. Then, $(2r)^2 = 17^2 - 1^2 = 16 \cdot 18$. Hence, $r^2 = 72$. Thus, $r = 6\sqrt{2}$.

112. The answer is (C). Let's use Heron's formula. First, $s = \frac{13+14+15}{2} = 21$. Then, the area equals $\sqrt{21(21-13)(21-14)(21-15)} = \sqrt{21 \cdot 8 \cdot 7 \cdot 6} = 84$.

113. The answer is (A). The sum of exterior angles of any polygon is $360°$. This can be proven using the fact that the sum of the measures of the interior angles of a polygon is equal to $(n-2) \times 180°$, where n is the number of sides of the polygon. To prove this, we can draw a polygon with n sides and draw a line segment from each vertex to the next vertex. These segments will form n exterior angles, and the sum of the measures of these angles will be $360°$.

114. The answer is (B). It is clear that $\triangle ADE \sim \triangle ECB$. Hence, we get $EC = 4.5$ from $AD : DE = 3 : 2 = EC : BC$. Thus, the area must be $\frac{13}{2} \times 3 = \frac{39}{2}$. The sum of m and n must be 41.

Here is another way to solve it. Let $EC = k$. Then, $AE^2 + BE^2 = AB^2$ implies that $(\sqrt{13})^2 + (9 + k^2) = (2+k)^2$, so $k = \frac{9}{2}$. Thus, the area of $ABCD$ must be $\frac{13}{2} \times 3 = \frac{39}{2}$.

115. The answer is (B). Let $BD = x$ and $CF = y$. According to the power of points theorem, we get $6^2 = 4(4+x)$ and $4^2 = y(y+6)$. Hence, $x = 5$ and $y = 2$. Thus, the perimeter of $\triangle ABC$ must be $8 + 9 + 10 = 27$.

116. The answer is (B). Since $m\angle ADB = 120°$ and $AD = BD$, we get $m\angle CBE = 90°$. Hence, $BC = 5\sqrt{3}$, $BE = 15$, and $CE = 10\sqrt{3}$.

117. The answer is (D). The law of syllogism is a rule of reasoning in logic that states that if two statements are made, and the first one implies the second one, and the second one implies a third one, then the first statement implies the third one. It is a form of deductive reasoning that allows one to infer a conclusion from two premises. According to the law of syllogism and contrapositives, we conclude with (D).

118. The answer is (C). The central angle measure must be $108°$. Thus, the length of the minor arc formed must be $2\pi(10) \times \frac{108°}{360°} = 6\pi$. Therefore, the major arc has the length of 14π.

119. The answer is (C). Let the half chord's length be k. Then, $k^2 = 25^2 - 7^2 = 24^2$. Therefore, $k = 24$. The length of the actual chord must be 48.

120. The answer is (C). Let $CP = k$. According to the angle bisector theorem with proper extension of $\overline{AB}$, we get $k + 2 : k = 4 : 3$, which means $4k = 3(k+2) = 3k + 6$. Therefore, $k = 6$.

121. The answer is (C). Let the measure of one exterior angle be θ. Then, we can easily deduce that $\theta = 36°$. According to the exterior angle property, we get $36° \times n = 360°$, where n is the number of sides in a regular polygon. Hence, $n = 10$.

122. The answer is (A). The area of the circle must be 4π. However, the area of the equilateral triangle must be $\frac{\sqrt{3}}{4}(2\sqrt{3})^2 = 3\sqrt{3}$. Thus, $4\pi - 3\sqrt{3}$ must be the area inside the circle but outside the triangle.

123. The answer is (A). Let k be the half the length of shorter diagonal. Then, $k^2 + 64 = 100$, so $k = 6$. Hence, the area of rhombus must be $\frac{1}{2} \times 12 \times 16 = 96$.

124. The answer is (C). Two circles are similar if and only if their radii are in proportion. This means that if one circle has a radius that is twice as long as the radius of another circle, then the two circles are similar. Hence, the square of length ratio determines the area ratio. Since the radius is doubled, the area ratio must be quadrupled.

125. The answer is (B). Using similarity, the area of the smallest right triangle can be $\frac{9}{25} \times 6 = \frac{54}{25}$ because the length ratio between the smallest right triangle and the largest one equals 3 to 5, if we look at the lengths of hypotenuses.

126. The answer is (C). Given a chord on a circle, we should cut it into half by drawing a perpendicular bisector through its midpoint. All the midpoints will form a circle with its diameter $\overline{OA}$.

127. The answer is (B). Let $l : w = 3 : 2$. Then, $l = 3k$ and $w = 2k$ for some real k. Then, $lw = (3k)(2k) = 6k^2 = 96$, so $k^2 = 16$. Thus, $k = 4$. Since the perimeter equals $2(l + w) = 2(5k) = 10k$, we conclude that the value must be 40.

128. The answer is (C). The bisector cuts the opposite side into segments of length ratio 12 to 18. Hence, let the smaller and larger length be $12k$ and $18k$ for some k. Then, $30k = 25$, so $k = \frac{5}{6}$. Therefore, the difference between the lengths must be $18k - 12k = 6k = 5$.

129. The answer is (B). Let half the diagonals have lengths of $2k$ and $3k$, respectively. Then, $(2k)^2 + (3k)^2 = 169$. Thus, $13k^2 = 169$. Since the area of the rhombus can be written as $\frac{1}{2} \times (4k) \times (6k) = 12k^2 = 12(13) = 156$.

130. The answer is (A). The hypotenuse must have the length of 10. Hence, the right triangle must have 5 and $5\sqrt{3}$ as their lengths. Since $\overline{BC}$ must be the opposite side of $60°$, we can conclude that $BC > AC$. Thus, $BC = 5\sqrt{3}$.

131. The answer is (D). Since the triangle has its base and area fixed, the height must be fixed. In a plane, the third vertex (the vertex opposite the base) must stay either above or below the base. Thus, there are two parallel lines such that the distance between any of the lines and the segment (the base) equals the height of the given triangle. This is because the height is a perpendicular line to the base, if the base is fixed, the height can only go above or below it.

132. The answer is (C). This is a typical right isosceles triangle. Hence, the ratio between the longer hypotenuse to the shorter leg must be $\sqrt{2}$ to 1.

133. The answer is (C). Since $\frac{1}{2} \times$ base $\times (x+3) = 2x^2 + 5x - 3$, we get **base** $= 4x - 2$ by performing a long division.

134. The answer is (B). Either using the power of points or Pythagorean Theorem, we conclude that CD is cut into 2 and 32. Hence, $OE = 15$.

135. The answer is (B). Let $DB = k$. Then, $k^2 = (\frac{3}{2})^2 + (5 - \frac{3\sqrt{3}}{2})^2 = 34 - 15\sqrt{3}$. Thus, $a + b + c = 34 + 15 + 3 = 34 + 18 = 52$.

136. The answer is (B). Regardless of whether $\overline{BC}$ is a diameter, we always get $m\angle ACB = 45°$, according to the ratio between the inscribed angle and the central angle.

137. The answer is (B). $m\angle AEB = \frac{90° - 40°}{2} = 25°$.

138. The answer is (C). The height of a smaller equilateral triangle, six of which consist of the regular hexagon, can be written as $2\sqrt{3}$. Hence, the side length must be 4.

139. The answer is (D). According to the power of points, $4 \times 5 = 2 \times CE$, so $CE = 10$.

140. The answer is (D). According to the power of points, we get $4 \times 5 = 2 \times CE$, so $CE = 10$.

141. The answer is (A). This is the definition of perpendicular bisector. A perpendicular bisector is a line or a plane that is perpendicular to and bisects (divides into two equal parts) a line segment. In other words, it is a line that goes through the midpoint of a line segment and is perpendicular to that line segment. The line segment is the segment that is bisected.

142. The answer is (C). Remember that the circumdiameter of a right triangle is always its hypotenuse. This can be proven by drawing a right triangle and marking the circumcenter, which is the midpoint of the hypotenuse. It's clear that the hypotenuse is the longest distance between any two points on the triangle, and it goes through the circumcenter, which is the center of its circumcircle.

This theorem is known as the circumdiameter of a right triangle theorem and can be used to find the length of the hypotenuse of a right triangle if the lengths of the legs are known. It also can be used to prove properties of right triangles.

143. The answer is (D). It is clear that O is its centroid. Hence, $AO : OA' = 2 : 1$. Let $AO = 2k$ and $OA' = k$, such that $2k + k = 3k = 12$. Thus, $k = 4$. We conclude that $AO = 2k = 8$.

144. The answer is (C). Menelaus' theorem is a statement in Euclidean geometry that states that in any triangle and any transversal that intersects the three sides of the triangle, the product of the directed ratios of the segments of the transversal to the corresponding segments of the triangle stays constant. According to the theorem, $\frac{AF}{BF} \times \frac{BC}{CE} \times \frac{ED}{AD} = 1$. Thus, $\frac{ED}{AD} = \frac{1}{4}$. Hence, $\frac{AD}{ED} = \frac{4}{1}$, so $m + n = 4 + 1 = 5$.

145. The answer is (C). A regular decagon has 10 vertices to choose. Hence, out of 10 vertices, we must choose 4 vertices to form a quadrilateral. There are $\binom{10}{4}$ number of quadrilaterals formed, where $\binom{10}{4} = \frac{10 \cdot 9 \cdot 8 \cdot 7}{4 \cdot 3 \cdot 2 \cdot 1} = 210$.

146. The answer is (A). Given a cyclic quadrilateral, any three adjacent vertices form a triangle circumscribed about the same circle. It is easy to find out that the circumcenters of the three triangles formed by the three adjacent vertices of a cyclic quadrilateral all coincide at a single point. This is because the circumcenter of a triangle is the center of the circle that circumscribes the triangle and since these three triangles are all tangent to the same circle, so their circumcenters will be at the center of that circle.

This property of a cyclic quadrilateral is known as the "Common Internal Tangents" or "Common Internal Secant" theorem. It is useful in solving geometric problems and proving properties of cyclic quadrilaterals.

147. The answer is (B). Since the height is 12, we can deduce that the side length must be $8\sqrt{3}$. Thus, the area must be $\frac{\sqrt{3}}{4}(8\sqrt{3})^2 = \frac{\sqrt{3}}{4} \times (64 \cdot 3) = 48\sqrt{3}$. Hence, $a\sqrt{b} = 48\sqrt{3}$, so $a + b = 48 + 3 = 51$.

148. The answer is (C). Cut the chord into half by drawing a diameter passing through its midpoint. Then, we can easily deduce that $r^2 = 208$ by Pythagorean Theorem. The area of circle can be written as $\pi(r^2) = 208\pi$. Thus, $k = 208$.

149. The answer is (D). Let the centroid be R. Then, $AR = BR = 4$, and $PR = QR = 2$. Since the two given medians form a right angle, we conclude that $[ARB] = 8$, $[AQR] = [BPR] = 4$. Since $CQ = AQ$ and $CP = BP$, we also conclude that $[CQR] = [CPR] = 4$. Therefore, the area of $\triangle ABC$ must be 24.

150. The answer is (B). Let D be the perpendicular foot from A to $\overline{BC}$. Drawing ω_1 and ω_2 nicely, we get the two points of intersection are A and D. Since $AD = 12$, we conclude that the answer is (B), using circumdiameters' diameters as right triangles' hypotenuses.

Part 2

Solution Manual

for 150 Problems

001. The answer is (B). A plane is a geometric object that can be thought of as an infinitely large, flat surface that extends indefinitely in all directions without any edges or boundaries. It is a two-dimensional object, which means it has only length and width but no thickness. It is also a mathematical concept that can be described using equations and coordinates.

002. The answer is (D). Three non-collinear points, also known as three points that are not on the same line, are used to define a unique plane in geometry. This is because a plane is defined as the set of all points that are equidistant from the three given points. The three points determine the position of the plane in space and the distance between the plane and each of the points.

However, if the three points are collinear, they do not form a unique plane. This is because collinear points lie on the same line and there are infinitely many planes that pass through a line. Imagine a piece of paper that is rotating along the line in its middle. The paper can rotate to any angle, and in each angle, it forms a different plane that passes through the line of the three collinear points.

In other words, if the three points are collinear, they don't define a unique plane because any plane that goes through the line determined by these points will pass through these three points. In contrast, if three non-collinear points are given, there is only one plane that passes through these three points.

003. The answer is (C). There are four distinct points in the figure. Choose the first point out of the four points. Then, choose the second point out of the three remaining points. Hence, there are 4×3 pairs. However, the segment can be labeled in reverse order, so we must get rid of the overcounts. Thus, the answer must be 6.

004. The answer is (C). Fix a vertex, let's say A. Then, connect it with adjacent vertices to find out there are three types of segments that can be drawn from A. The first must be the segment congruent to the side of regular hexagon. The second must be the segment congruent to shorter diagonal of the regular hexagon. The last must be the segment congruent to the longest diagonal of the figure.

005. The answer is (D). From the given condition, we set $AB = CD$. Hence, $2x - 1 = 3x - 4$ implies that $x = 3$. This means that $AB = CD = 5$. Since $AB + CD = 5 + 5$, by substitution, we conclude that $AB + CD = 10$.

006. The answer is (D). Let $AB = CD$, according to the given condition. Then, $3 - 2x = 3x - 7$ implies that $x = 2$. However, the segment has its length at least 0. if $x = 2$, $AB = CD = -1$, which contradicts the assumption that any segment has non-negative length. Therefore, there is no such x value satisfying the given condition.

007. The answer is (B). Let x be the coordinate of C. Then, $AC = x - 5$ and $CB = 10 - x$, according to the definition of absolute value on a real number line. Hence, $x - 5 : 10 - x = 2 : 3$ implies that $20 - 2x = 3x - 15$. Therefore, $5x = 35$, implying that $x = 7$. Since $5 < 7 < 10$, the coordinate of C must be 7.

008. The answer is (D). Let c be the coordinate of C. First, assume that C is between A and B. Then, $AC : CB = 2 : 3$ implies that $c - 2 : 12 - c = 2 : 3$. Hence, $c = 6$. Second, assume that C is not between A and B. Then, $AC : CB = 2 : 3$ implies that $2 - c : 12 - c = 2 : 3$. Hence, $c = -18$. The sum of all possible coordinates of c is -12. Such coordinates we found are known as the intersection points between the line containing A and B and the circle of Apollonius. Another way to solve this problem is to translate $(A, B) = (2, 10)$ into $(A', B') = (0, 10)$ such that the interior point turns out to be 4 and the exterior point -20. We may translate the points 2 units right again to conclude that c is either 6 or -18.

009. The answer is (D). Draw auxiliary lines − vertical and horizontal lines − at the three given points. Then, the resulting figure has a rectangle of area 8. Get rid of three right triangles of area 2, 1, and 2. Hence, the area of triangle formed by the three points must be 3. Similar to question 27 and 28, one may use Shoelace Theorem to compute the area of the triangle.

The shoelace theorem, also known as the Gauss area formula, is a mathematical result that can be used to determine the area of a simple polygon. A simple polygon is a polygon with no self-intersections, which means the sides do not cross over each other.

The shoelace theorem states that the area of a simple polygon can be calculated by taking the sum of the product of the x-coordinates of the vertices and the y-coordinates of the vertices that follow them, and subtracting the sum of the product of the y-coordinates of the vertices and the x-coordinates of the vertices that follow them. This is how we use Shoelace Theorem. Given the coordinates $(1, 1)$, $(3, 3)$ and $(2, 5)$, we get $\frac{1}{2} \times |(1 \cdot 3 + 3 \cdot 5 + 2 \cdot 1) - (1 \cdot 3 + 3 \cdot 2 + 5 \cdot 1)| = \frac{1}{2} \times |20 - 14| = 3$.

The shoelace theorem can also be extended to calculate the centroid of a polygon. A centroid is the geometric center of a polygon, and it can be represented as (C_x, C_y). The centroid of a polygon can be found by taking the average of x-coordinates and y-coordinates of the vertices of the polygon. It is important to note that the shoelace theorem is only applicable for simple polygon, if the polygon is self-intersecting or concave, the shoelace theorem will not work.

010. The answer is (A). We apply the equivalent strategies as in the previous question. The resulting figure has a rectangle of area 20. Get rid of four right triangles of area 2, 1.5, 3, and 3. Hence, the area of quadrilateral formed by the four points must be 10.5.

011. The answer is (A). The difference in x-values is 3 and that in y-values is 4. Thus, the distance between the two points equals $\sqrt{3^2 + 4^2} = \sqrt{25} = 5$.

012. The answer is (B). According to the taxicab metric, the distance between A and B can be computed as the sum of the difference in x-values and that in y-values, which equals 7. In other words, the horizontal translation of 4 units and the vertical translation of 3 units are combined as 7 units of movement.

013. The answer is (C). Imagine a right triangle that stands in a space. The bottom side has the length of $\sqrt{1^2 + 1^2} = \sqrt{2}$. Since the height of the triangle equals 2, we may use the pythagorean theorem such that

$$OA = \sqrt{(\sqrt{2})^2 + 2^2} = \sqrt{2 + 4} = \sqrt{6}.$$

014. The answer is (B). Along with the previous question, we may conclude that the distance formula can be extended to space points, i.e.,

$$\sqrt{(3-1)^2 + (4-2)^2 + (6-3)^2} = \sqrt{4+4+9} = \sqrt{17}$$

015. The answer is (C). Two angles are complementary if and only if the sum of their measures equals $90°$. Hence,

$$m\angle A + m\angle B = 30° - x + 45° + 2x = 75° + x = 90°$$

Thus, $x = 15°$.

016. The answer is (D). The set of points equidistant from two intersecting lines in a plane is known as the angle bisector line of the angles formed by the two lines. This is because the angle bisector line divides the angle formed by the two lines into two congruent angles.

The vertical angle congruence postulate states that if two lines intersect, then the opposite angles formed are congruent, or equal in measure. This means that if two lines intersect, they form two pairs of congruent angles. One pair of these angles is formed by the angle bisectors of the two lines. Since these angle bisectors divide the angles formed by the two lines into congruent angles, they are also congruent.

As a result, there are two "perpendicular" lines formed by the angle bisectors of the two intersecting lines. These perpendicular lines are called angle bisectors. The two angle bisectors are perpendicular to each other because they are formed by the intersection of two lines that form a right angle at the point of intersection, due to the vertical angle congruence postulate.

017. The answer is (A). If three distinct planes in space are to intersect, there are two possibilities for the shape of their intersection: a straight line or a single point.

The first possibility is that the three planes have a common line among themselves. This means that all three planes intersect at a single straight line, which is the intersection of the three planes. This line is also known as the line of intersection of the three planes. The line of intersection is the set of all points that are common to all three planes.

The second possibility is that the three planes meet up at a single point. This means that the three planes intersect at a single point, which is the intersection of the three planes. This point is also known as the point of intersection of the three planes. The point of intersection is the set of all points that are common to all three planes. To illustrate this, imagine a typical xyz-plane. The origin $O(0,0,0)$ is the common point of intersection of the x, y, and z-plane. This point is the point of intersection of the three planes because it is a point that belongs to all three planes.

018. The answer is (B). The statement that "two distinct points always form a unique line passing through the two" is known as the first postulate of Euclidean geometry, which states that any two distinct points in space can be connected by a straight line, and that this line is unique. Similarly, the statement that "given any line, one may always find two distinct points that would have resulted in graphing that line" is known as the second postulate of Euclidean geometry. This postulate states that for any given line, there are always two distinct points that can be used to define it.

The statement "three non-collinear points form a unique plane" is also a fundamental postulate of Euclidean geometry. This postulate states that any three non-collinear points in space can be used to define a unique plane. Likewise, given any plane, one may spot three non-collinear points that would have formed it. This means that for any given plane, there are always three non-collinear points that can be used to define it.

019.

(a) It is true. Non-adjacent angles can be complementary as long as the sum of their measures equal to $90°$.

(b) It is true. This is a definition of linear pair. Linear pair implies that the angles in such pair are adjacent and supplementary at the same time.

(c) It is false. Three collinear points never form a unique plane. Also, there is no phrase about three distinct points. One may argue that three indistinct points do not determine a unique plane.

(d) It is false. Some two non-parallel lines in space are skew, never meeting at a point.

(e) It is true. Two distinct planes that are not parallel to one another will eventually meet at a line.

(f) It is false. There exists only one line passing through two distinct points. Since there is at least one counter-example to the given statement, it is false.

020.

(a) It is false. Consider $x = -\sqrt{3}$, which satisfies the hypothesis, but not the conclusion.

(b) It is false. Any real number has its square greater than or equal to 0. Hence, the hypothesis is always satisfied, yet the conclusion will always stay false.

(c) It is true. At $x = 1$, both hypothesis and conclusion are true. Mathematical statement is true if both are true. One may refer to the Law of Detachment.

(d) It is true. This is a contrapositive statement of (c). Since the truth value for the original statement and its contrapositive do not change, we may safely conclude that this is true.

(e) It is false. There are two values $x = \pm 1$ satisfying the hypothesis, but there is only one value in the conclusion. Hence, the hypothesis is satisfied at $x = -1$, but the conclusion is false. Hence, $x = -1$ is the counterexample to the given statement.

(f) It is false because this is a contrapositive of (e).

021. The answer is (B). According to the segment additional postulate, $AB + BC = AC$, since A, B, and C are collinear.

022. The answer is (C). According to triangular inequality, $AC + BC > AB$. If A, C, and B are collinear, then $AC + BC = AB$. However, since C is not on the line containing A and B, then a triangle ABC must be formed to satisfy triangular inequality.

023. The answer is (B). Let the coordinate of B be k. Then, $AB = k - 3$ and $BC = 10 - k$. Hence, $AB : BC = k - 3 : 10 - k = 4 : 7$ implies that $k = \dfrac{61}{11}$. Hence, $m + n = 61 + 11 = 72$.

024. The answer is (C). Since $2(2x - 10) = 3x + 1$, we get $x = 21$. Thus, $m\angle DAC = (2(21) - 10)° = 32°$.

025. The answer is (C). The line containing $(3, 4)$ that is perpendicular to $y = x$ has the equation $x + y = 7$. Hence, the intersection point between $y = x$ and $x + y = 7$ is $(3.5, 3.5)$. The distance between $(3, 4)$ and $(3.5, 3.5)$ equals $\sqrt{(0.5)^2 + (0.5)^2} = \sqrt{0.5} = \sqrt{2}/2$.

Here is another way to solve this problem. Let t be the distance from $(3, 4)$ to $y = x$. Then, we use similar triangles to set up a ratio expression.

$$t : 1 = 3 : 3\sqrt{2}$$
$$3 = 3\sqrt{2}t$$
$$t = \frac{1}{\sqrt{2}}$$

026. The answer is (D). Using the coordinate geometry, we find out the vertical distance between the lines is 4 and the horizontal distance is 2. Hence, we are simply looking for the height to the hyptoneuse of a right triangle whose lengths are 2 and 4. Let such height be d. Then, $d = \frac{4}{\sqrt{5}}$, since the length of its hypotenuse is $2\sqrt{5}$, and its area is 4. Since $\frac{m}{n} = d^2 = \frac{16}{5}$, where 16 and 5 are relatively prime positive integers, the sum of m and n is 21.

027. The answer is (B). The base length must be 2, whereas the height must be 2. The area of a newly formed triangle is $\frac{1}{2} \times 2 \times 2 = 2$.

028. The answer is (C). According to shoelace theorem, the parallelogram formed by A, B, and C has the area of 9. Therefore, the triangle area must be $\frac{9}{2}$.

029. The answer is (A). Let $k - d$, k, and $k + d$ be the measures of interior angles. Then, $k = 60°$. Hence, $0 < 60 - d$ and $60 + d < 180$. Hence, $d < 60$. Since d must be integer, $d = 1, 2, 3, \cdots, 59$.

030. The answer is (A). According to the exterior angle theorem, the sum of measures of two remote angles equals the measure of exterior angle. Hence,
$41 - 2x + 2x + 43 = 84$.

031. The answer is (A). The circumcenter of a triangle is a point that is equidistant from all three vertices of the triangle. It is the center of the circle that passes through all three vertices of the triangle, which is called the circumcircle.

032. The answer is (B). The incenter of a triangle is a point that is equidistant from the three sides of the triangle. It is the center of the circle inscribed in the triangle, which is a circle that is tangent to all three sides of the triangle at their points of concurrency. One way to find the incenter of a triangle is by looking for the point of concurrency among the angle bisectors of the triangle's interior angles. An angle bisector is a line that divides an angle into two congruent angles. By drawing the angle bisectors of all three interior angles of the triangle, we can find the point where they intersect, which is the incenter of the triangle.

033. The answer is (A). Consider SSA ambiguous case. The answer choice (A) may produce SSA ambiguous case.

034. The answer is (B). The sum of exterior angles of the figure in the question, in fact, all planar convex polygons, must be 360°.

035. The answer is (D). Similar figures have a fixed ratio of sides and congruent corresponding angles. Hence, the fixed ratio is not necessarily 1.

036. The answer is (B). Since tangents are congruent to one another, $3x - 1 = 5$ implies that $x = 2$.

037. The answer is (C). Equilateral triangles can be expressed as isosceles triangles whose vertex angle measure equals 60°. All equilateral triangles are similar but not always congruent, though it might not be necessarily referenced.

038. The answer is (C). If lines are parallel, then we may use alternate interior angle theorem(or postulate) such that any alternate interior angle pair consists of congruent angles. The alternate interior angle theorem states that if two lines are parallel, then any pair of alternate interior angles are congruent, or equal in measure. Alternate interior angles are angles that are on opposite sides of a transversal line and are between the two parallel lines.

This theorem is based on the fact that when two lines are parallel, the alternate interior angles are formed by the intersection of the transversal line with the two parallel lines. These angles are congruent because they are formed by the intersection of the same transversal line with the two parallel lines.

039. The answer is (C). The volume of a sphere must be $\frac{4}{3}\pi r^3$.

040. The answer is (B). The sum of radii equals the distance between the centers. Hence, there is only one point of intersection between the two circles.

041. The answer is (C). It is obvious that $AB < AC$ and $BC < AC$ because of side-angle theorem. Larger interior angle produces larger opposite side length.

042. The answer is (B). Using Pythagorean Theorem, we may find that $PQ = 2\sqrt{10}$. Due to congruent tangents, we get $PS = SR = SQ = \sqrt{10}$.

043. The answer is (B). In an isosceles triangle, angle bisectors of the base angles are congruent due to ASA congruence postulate and CPCTC, which stands for "Corresponding Parts of Congruent Triangles are Congruent." This is a theorem in Euclidean geometry that states that if two triangles are congruent, then all corresponding parts of the two triangles are also congruent.

Likewise, the ASA (Angle-Side-Angle) postulate is a statement in Euclidean geometry that states that if in two triangles, two angles and the included side of one triangle are congruent to two corresponding angles and the included side of another triangle, then the two triangles are congruent.

044. The answer is (C). Since a regular pentagon can be formed by connecting three triangles, the sum of interior angle measures must be 540°.

045. The answer is (D). Triangle ABC and MBN are similar due to SAS similarity. Hence, $MN : BC = 1 : 2$. Since $BC = 8$, we conclude that $MN = 4$.

046. The answer is (B). The set of vertices whose base equals $\overline{AB}$ must stay on the perpendicular bisector of $\overline{AB}$. Since perpendicular bisector is a line, the answer must be (B).

047. The answer is (D). Diagonals of a quadrilateral are bisected if and only if the polygon is a parallelogram. A parallelogram is a quadrilateral that has opposite sides parallel and congruent, and opposite angles are congruent. When the diagonals of a parallelogram are drawn, they bisect each other at their midpoint. This is because the diagonals of a parallelogram are both medians and altitudes of the quadrilateral, and medians and altitudes of any shape bisect each other.

048. The answer is (B). The measure of segment $\overline{AB}$ can be at most the diameter of a circle. Hence, the chord length must be smaller than or equal to the diameter length.

049. The answer is (D). Given a chord connecting two points on the circle, its perpendicular bisector always passes through the center, containing the diameter.

050. The answer is (D). If folded into half along the line of symmetry, the figure must be completely overlapped. Hence, there are four such lines passing through the center.

051. The answer is (C). The sum of exterior angles of dodecagon must be $360°$.

052. The answer is (C). Altitude from B has its base $\overline{AC}$. Since $\angle C$ is right, the altitude is congruent to $\overline{BC}$.

053. The answer is (A). Since $2\pi r = 4$, we get $r = \frac{2}{\pi}$. Thus, the area of triangle must be $\pi r^2 = \frac{4}{\pi}$, which is closest to 1.

054. The answer is (C). A parallelepiped is a 3-dimensional geometric shape with six rectangular faces that are parallelograms. It is a rectangular prism with parallelogram faces. It is a polyhedron that has six faces that are parallelograms, and opposite faces are congruent. Special kind of parallelepiped is a prism, hence, prism and parallelepiped are equivalent kinds.

055. The answer is (D). Given a right triangle, its hypotenuse is always equal to its circumdiameter. Hence, we are looking for the circumcenter of the right triangle. Hence, it must be the midpoint of the hypotenuse, which can easily be found by the point of concurrency among perpendicular bisectors of all sides.

056. The answer is (B). The only answer choice that may have been true is (C), but if two lines are skew, then they are not parallel.

057. The answer is (C). This is simply the definition of contrapositive of the original mathematical statement.

058. The answer is (B). The base area must be $\sqrt{3}$, and it height must be $\frac{\sqrt{8}}{\sqrt{3}}$, which can be found by applying Pythagorean Theorem. Hence, the volume must be $\frac{1}{3} \times \sqrt{3} \times \frac{\sqrt{8}}{\sqrt{3}} = \frac{2\sqrt{2}}{3}$. Hence, $a + b + c = 2 + 2 + 3 = 7$.

059. The answer is (C). When we say that two planes are distinct, it means that they are not the same plane. They do not share the same set of points and do not have the same orientation in space. In other words, they are different planes that do not overlap. If we have two distinct planes, we can be sure that they cannot be identical. This is because planes that are identical would have to share the same set of points and have the same orientation in space, which is not possible for two distinct planes.

060. The answer is (C). The ratio between the inscribed angle measure and the central angle measure is 1 to 2. Hence, the ratio we want must be $\frac{2}{1} = 2$.

061. The answer is (B). If we let $AE = k$, then $k^2 + 4^2 = 5^2$ implies that $k = 3$. Hence, the lengths of bases are 19 and 10, and the height is 4. Thus, the area of trapezoid must be $\frac{1}{2} \times 4 \times (10 + 19) = 58$.

062. The answer is (C). Given a fixed point, there exists a sphere equidistant from the point. Imagine this sphere rotating around the given line as its axis of movement. Its trace must result in a cylinder-shaped figure that does not end.

063. The answer is (D). Since $OB = 12$, and $m\angle ABC = 120°$, we can conclude that $m\angle AOC = 60°$. By HL congruence, we get $m\angle AOB = m\angle COB = 30°$. Hence, $AO = OC = 6\sqrt{3}$, and $AB = BC = 6$.

064. The answer is (B). All squares are similar to one another. Since $BD : CD = \sqrt{2} : 1$, the area ratio must be $2 : 1$. Thus, the area of $BDEF$ must be twice that of $ABCD$, which means that the area of $BDEF$ is 6.

065. The answer is (C). According to similarities, $18 : MB = MB : 8$, so $MB^2 = 8 \times 18 = 12^2 = 144$. Hence, $MB = 12$.

066. The answer is (A). The shorter diagonal can be bisected into the segments of length 6. According to special right triangle property, we get the longer diagonal having the length of $12\sqrt{3}$. Thus, the side measure of the rhombus is 12.

067. The answer is (C). When we negate the hypothesis and the conclusion of a statement, we obtain a new statement that is called the inverse of the original statement. The inverse of a statement is formed by reversing the direction of the logical relationship between the hypothesis and the conclusion.

068. The answer is (D). Since X is the midpoint of $\overline{AB}$, we get $AX = BX$ and X between A and B.

069. The answer is (C). Given four different lines, we must choose two lines to form a unique plane. Hence, there are $\binom{4}{2} = \frac{4 \times 3}{2} = 6$ different planes formed by the lines.

070. The answer is (A). According to the special right triangle property, we use $1 : \sqrt{3} : 2$ to solve for the problem. Let k be the length of the shortest leg. Then, the other two lengths must be $k\sqrt{3}$ and $2k$. Since $2k = 10$, we get $k = 5$. There are two possible values of legs, i.e., 5 and $5\sqrt{3}$. Out of answer choices, (A) is the only answer choice that has one of the two values.

071. The answer is (D). Since the circumdiameter becomes the hypotenuse for the right isosceles triangle, we get the side length of the square as $2\sqrt{2}$. Thus, its area must be $(2\sqrt{2})^2 = 8$.

072. The answer is (D). Out of all answer choices, $QM : QF = \sqrt{3} : 2$, according to the special right triangle property. Hence, $QM^2 : QF^2 = 3 : 4$. Thus, (D) must be correct.

073. The answer is (D). When a line is given in space, we can draw a line that is perpendicular to it by finding a point on the given line and then drawing a line that is perpendicular to the given line and passing through that point. This can be done in infinitely many ways, by choosing different points on the given line, we can draw infinitely many lines that are perpendicular to it.

074. The answer is (C). First, the midpoint of -7 and 3 must be -2. Second, the midpoint of 6 and -4 is 1. Hence, the midpoint must be $(-2, 1)$.

075. The answer is (D). This is a basic application of midsegment theorem which states that in a triangle, the segment that connects the midpoints of two sides is parallel to the third side and is half the length of that side. In other words, in a triangle, the midsegment is parallel to the third side and its length is half the length of the third side. Hence, $\overline{DF}$ is parallel to $\overline{BC}$ and $DF : BC = 1 : 2$, due to SAS similarity.

076. The answer is (D). All answer choices except (D) are true due to similar triangles. However, $KP^2 \neq QK^2 + QP^2$.

077. The answer is (B). According to the power of point theorem, we get $AS \cdot SB = CS \cdot SD$. Hence, $2 \times 3 = k \times 4$. Therefore, $k = \frac{3}{2}$.

078. The answer is (D). Given perpendicular lines, label the lines as x-axis and y-axis. Then, the sum of the squares of the point's distances from the two axes can be identified as $x^2 + y^2$, if the point has the coordinates of (x, y). Hence, the locus must be a circle.

079. The answer is (D). Drop the perpendicular foot from the vertex opposite the longest side. Let its height be b, and the longest side be cut into segments of length a and $\sqrt{11} - a$. Hence, $a^2 + b^2 = 3$ and $(\sqrt{11} - a)^2 + b^2 = 8$. Then, $a = \frac{3}{\sqrt{11}}$. Thus, $b^2 = \frac{24}{11}$. Thus, the area must be $\frac{2\sqrt{6}}{2} = \sqrt{6}$.

080. The answer is (A). All equilateral triangles are similar to one another, so if we get the length ratio, we can easily get the area ratio. Since the side length of the larger triangle is twice that of the smaller triangle, we get the area ratio of $1:4$ or $4:1$. The only answer choice that matches with this conclusion is (A).

081. The answer is (C). Since $\triangle ACD \cong \triangle BDC$, we get $AD = BC = \sqrt{16-9} = \sqrt{7}$.

082. The answer is (C). This is a typical application of Pythagorean Theorem. The common internal tangent can be found by a right triangle whose hypotenuse has the length of 18 and height has the length of 9. Thus, the common internal tangent must have the length of $9\sqrt{3}$.

083. The answer is (B). An inscribed angle is an angle formed by two chords of a circle that share an endpoint on the circle. The central angle of a circle is an angle formed by two radii of the circle that share an endpoint on the circle. The ratio of inscribed angle measure and central angle measure is 1 to 2 means that for any inscribed angle in a circle, the measure of the inscribed angle is half the measure of the central angle that intercepts the same arc. Since the inscribed angle measure equals $20°$, we get the central angle measure of $40°$.

084. The answer is (C). According to the power of point, we get
$AB^2 = AD \cdot AC = 1 \cdot (1 + 2r) = 4$. Thence, $1 + 2r = 4$. Thus, $2r = 3$. Therefore, $r = \frac{3}{2}$.

085. The answer is (B). According to the angle bisector theorem, we get
$AC:BC = AD:BD$. Let $AD = 5k$, $BD = 4k$, and h be the height from C to $\overline{AB}$.
Thus, $[ACD]:[BCD] = \frac{5kh}{2} : 2kh$. Thus, $[ACD]:[BCD] = 5:4$.

086. The answer is (A). The chord is perpendicularly bisected by the diameter, which can be labeled as $8+x$, where 8 is the length of AE and x is that of the remaining part of the diameter. Hence, according to the power of point theorem, we get $8x = 16$. Thus, $x = 2$. Since the diameter has the length of 10, the radius has the length of 5.

087. The answer is (D). The locus of two intersecting lines in a plane that satisfy the given condition must be two perpendicular lines, different from the original lines.

088. The answer is (C). According to the property of isosceles trapezoid,
$CV:MV = 3:5$. Since $CM = 4$, we get $CV + MV = 3k + 5k = 4$. Thus, $k = \frac{1}{2}$,
implying that $MV = \frac{5}{2}$.

089. The answer is (C). Using the similar triangles inside the right triangle, let $2k$ be the length of its hypotenuse. Then, k and $k\sqrt{3}$ are its side lengths. Hence,
$\frac{1}{2} \times k \times k\sqrt{3} = \frac{1}{2} \times 2k \times 1$. Thus, $k = \frac{2\sqrt{3}}{3}$. Therefore, $2k = \frac{4\sqrt{3}}{3}$.

090. The answer is (A). Recall that the hypotenuse of a right triangle equals the circumdiameter of its circumcircle. The largest height can be the length of its radius. Thus, $\frac{1}{2} \times 6 \times 3 = 9$.

091. The answer is (B). Length chasing tells us that the central angle measure of AB is $30°$ and that of CD is $8°$. Hence, $m\angle CFD = \frac{30° - 8°}{2} = \frac{22°}{2} = 11°$.

092. The answer is (D). This is an application of midsegment theorem. $EF : \frac{27}{2} = 2 : 3$. Hence, $EF = 9$.

093. The answer is (C). The volume of a sphere must be $\frac{4\pi a^3}{3}$ and the volume of cylinder must be $\pi(\frac{\sqrt{2}a}{2})^2 \times \sqrt{2}a = \frac{2\sqrt{2}\pi a^3}{4}$. Hence, the volume ratio of cylinder to sphere must be $\frac{6\sqrt{2}}{18} = \frac{3\sqrt{2}}{8}$. Hence, $m + n + p = 13$.

094. The answer is (B). Let distances from P to all sides as x, y and z. Then, the area of the triangle can be written as $3(x + y + z)$. On the other hand, the area of equilateral triangle must be $\frac{\sqrt{3}}{4} \times 6^2 = 9\sqrt{3}$. Thus, $x + y + z = 3\sqrt{3}$.

095. The answer is (D). First, we chase lengths to find out the inradius of length 2. Or, we may have used the area method such that we cut the triangle into three triangles such that $12r = \frac{1}{2} \times 6 \times 8$. Either way, we get $r = 2$.

096. The answer is (C). Intersecting part forms two arcs whose central angle measure equals $120°$. Since the radii are 1 for both circles, we get $2\pi(1) \times \frac{120°}{360°} \times 2 = \frac{4\pi}{3}$.

097. The answer is (D). Label the height as k. This altitude will cut the base into two segments of length x and $12 - x$, where the segment of length x is closer to the side of length 9. Then, $x^2 + k^2 = 81$ and $(12 - x)^2 + k^2 = 25$. Hence, $x = \frac{25}{3}$. Thus, $k^2 = 9^2 - (\frac{25}{3})^2 = \frac{104}{9}$. Therefore, $k = \sqrt{\frac{104}{9}}$.

098. The answer is (C). Given a triangle with side lengths 5, 12, and 13, its circumdiameter equals its hypotenuse, since it is a right triangle.

099. The answer is (C). The perpendicular bisector of $\overline{AC}$ can be written as $y = \frac{2}{3}x$. The perpendicular bisector of $\overline{AB}$ can be written as $y = -3(x - 1) + 4 = -3x + 7$. Since $\frac{2}{3} = \frac{y}{x}$, let $y = 2k$ and $x = 3k$. Thus, $2k = -9k + 7$. Therefore, $k = \frac{7}{11}$. Hence, $x + y = 5k = \frac{35}{11}$. The sum of numerator and denominator in reduced form must be 46.

Here is another way to solve it. We may set up $AP^2 = BP^2 = CP^2$ for $P(x, y)$. Then, $(x + 2)^2 + (y - 3)^2 = (x - 4)^2 + (y - 5)^2 = (x - 2)^2 + (y + 3)^2$ implies that $4x - 6y + 13 = -4x + 6y + 13 = -8x - 10y + 41$. Thus, $2x = 3y$, $11y = 14$, so $x + y = \frac{5}{2}y = \frac{5}{2} \times \frac{14}{11} = \frac{35}{11}$.

100. The answer is (B). There are five regular polyhedra − tetrahedron, hexahedron, octahedron, dodecahedron, and icosahedron.

101. The answer is (C). A cyclic quadrilateral is a quadrilateral in which all four vertices lie on a single circle. A quadrilateral is cyclic if and only if the opposite angles are supplementary, meaning they add up to 180 degrees. The second property of a cyclic quadrilateral is that congruent inscribed angles produce similar triangles within the quadrilateral. An inscribed angle is an angle formed by two chords of a circle that share an endpoint on the circle. When two inscribed angles in a cyclic quadrilateral are congruent, the triangles formed by the inscribed angles and the chord of the angle are similar.

102. The answer is (D). Orthocenter may stay within the figure or outside the figure. Similarly, the circumcenter may stay within or outside the figure. However, the centroid or incenter must stay inside the figure.

103. The answer is (A). The sector area can be written as $\pi r^2 \times \frac{108°}{360°} = 30\pi$. Hence, $r = 10$. Since r refers to the side length of the pentagon, we conclude that the side length must be 10.

104. The answer is (B). Imagine cutting four right isosceles triangles from a square whose side length must be $4 + 2\sqrt{2}$. Hence, $(4 + 2\sqrt{2})^2 - 4 \times (\frac{1}{2} \times 2 \times 2) = 16 + 16\sqrt{2} + 8 - 8 = 16 + 16\sqrt{2}$. The answer must be 34.

105. The answer is (B). Using special right triangle property, we get $AC = 5$, $BC = 5\sqrt{3}$ and $AB = 10$ because the median from C to $\overline{AB}$ is circumradius of $\triangle ABC$.

106. The answer is (D). The angle bisector cuts the longest side into segments with the ratio of 12 to 18. Label the shorter one as $12k$ and the longer one as $18k$. The sum must be $30k = 20$. Hence, $k = \frac{2}{3}$. Thus, $12k = 8$ and $18k = 12$. The two segments have the lengths of 8 and 12.

107. The answer is (C). If the supplementary angles are non-adjacent, then the figure is cyclic, but not necessarily a parallelogram.

108. The answer is (B). If $AB = 12$, then $MT = 6$. Since P is the midpoint of $\overline{CD}$, we get $PD = CP = 6$. Thus, $TF = EM = 3$, by similar figures of length ratio of 1 to 2.

109. The answer is (D). This is a definition of circumcenter.

110. The answer is (C). This is a definition of incenter.

111. The answer is (C). Let r be the radius. Then, $(2r)^2 = 17^2 - 1^2 = 16 \cdot 18$. Hence, $r^2 = 72$. Thus, $r = 6\sqrt{2}$.

112. The answer is (C). Let's use Heron's formula. First, $s = \frac{13+14+15}{2} = 21$. Then, the area equals $\sqrt{21(21-13)(21-14)(21-15)} = \sqrt{21 \cdot 8 \cdot 7 \cdot 6} = 84$.

113. The answer is (A). The sum of exterior angles of any polygon is $360°$. This can be proven using the fact that the sum of the measures of the interior angles of a polygon is equal to $(n-2) \times 180°$, where n is the number of sides of the polygon. To prove this, we can draw a polygon with n sides and draw a line segment from each vertex to the next vertex. These segments will form n exterior angles, and the sum of the measures of these angles will be $360°$.

114. The answer is (B). It is clear that $\triangle ADE \sim \triangle ECB$. Hence, we get $EC = 4.5$ from $AD : DE = 3 : 2 = EC : BC$. Thus, the area must be $\frac{13}{2} \times 3 = \frac{39}{2}$. The sum of m and n must be 41.

Here is another way to solve it. Let $EC = k$. Then, $AE^2 + BE^2 = AB^2$ implies that $(\sqrt{13})^2 + (9 + k^2) = (2+k)^2$, so $k = \frac{9}{2}$. Thus, the area of $ABCD$ must be $\frac{13}{2} \times 3 = \frac{39}{2}$.

115. The answer is (B). Let $BD = x$ and $CF = y$. According to the power of points theorem, we get $6^2 = 4(4+x)$ and $4^2 = y(y+6)$. Hence, $x = 5$ and $y = 2$. Thus, the perimeter of $\triangle ABC$ must be $8 + 9 + 10 = 27$.

116. The answer is (B). Since $m\angle ADB = 120°$ and $AD = BD$, we get $m\angle CBE = 90°$. Hence, $BC = 5\sqrt{3}$, $BE = 15$, and $CE = 10\sqrt{3}$.

117. The answer is (D). The law of syllogism is a rule of reasoning in logic that states that if two statements are made, and the first one implies the second one, and the second one implies a third one, then the first statement implies the third one. It is a form of deductive reasoning that allows one to infer a conclusion from two premises. According to the law of syllogism and contrapositives, we conclude with (D).

118. The answer is (C). The central angle measure must be $108°$. Thus, the length of the minor arc formed must be $2\pi(10) \times \frac{108°}{360°} = 6\pi$. Therefore, the major arc has the length of 14π.

119. The answer is (C). Let the half chord's length be k. Then, $k^2 = 25^2 - 7^2 = 24^2$. Therefore, $k = 24$. The length of the actual chord must be 48.

120. The answer is (C). Let $CP = k$. According to the angle bisector theorem with proper extension of $\overline{AB}$, we get $k + 2 : k = 4 : 3$, which means $4k = 3(k+2) = 3k + 6$. Therefore, $k = 6$.

121. The answer is (C). Let the measure of one exterior angle be θ. Then, we can easily deduce that $\theta = 36°$. According to the exterior angle property, we get $36° \times n = 360°$, where n is the number of sides in a regular polygon. Hence, $n = 10$.

122. The answer is (A). The area of the circle must be 4π. However, the area of the equilateral triangle must be $\frac{\sqrt{3}}{4}(2\sqrt{3})^2 = 3\sqrt{3}$. Thus, $4\pi - 3\sqrt{3}$ must be the area inside the circle but outside the triangle.

123. The answer is (A). Let k be the half the length of shorter diagonal. Then, $k^2 + 64 = 100$, so $k = 6$. Hence, the area of rhombus must be $\frac{1}{2} \times 12 \times 16 = 96$.

124. The answer is (C). Two circles are similar if and only if their radii are in proportion. This means that if one circle has a radius that is twice as long as the radius of another circle, then the two circles are similar. Hence, the square of length ratio determines the area ratio. Since the radius is doubled, the area ratio must be quadrupled.

125. The answer is (B). Using similarity, the area of the smallest right triangle can be $\frac{9}{25} \times 6 = \frac{54}{25}$ because the length ratio between the smallest right triangle and the largest one equals 3 to 5, if we look at the lengths of hypotenuses.

126. The answer is (C). Given a chord on a circle, we should cut it into half by drawing a perpendicular bisector through its midpoint. All the midpoints will form a circle with its diameter $\overline{OA}$.

127. The answer is (B). Let $l : w = 3 : 2$. Then, $l = 3k$ and $w = 2k$ for some real k. Then, $lw = (3k)(2k) = 6k^2 = 96$, so $k^2 = 16$. Thus, $k = 4$. Since the perimeter equals $2(l + w) = 2(5k) = 10k$, we conclude that the value must be 40.

128. The answer is (C). The bisector cuts the opposite side into segments of length ratio 12 to 18. Hence, let the smaller and larger length be $12k$ and $18k$ for some k. Then, $30k = 25$, so $k = \frac{5}{6}$. Therefore, the difference between the lengths must be $18k - 12k = 6k = 5$.

129. The answer is (B). Let half the diagonals have lengths of $2k$ and $3k$, respectively. Then, $(2k)^2 + (3k)^2 = 169$. Thus, $13k^2 = 169$. Since the area of the rhombus can be written as $\frac{1}{2} \times (4k) \times (6k) = 12k^2 = 12(13) = 156$.

130. The answer is (A). The hypotenuse must have the length of 10. Hence, the right triangle must have 5 and $5\sqrt{3}$ as their lengths. Since $\overline{BC}$ must be the opposite side of $60°$, we can conclude that $BC > AC$. Thus, $BC = 5\sqrt{3}$.

131. The answer is (D). Since the triangle has its base and area fixed, the height must be fixed. In a plane, the third vertex (the vertex opposite the base) must stay either above or below the base. Thus, there are two parallel lines such that the distance between any of the lines and the segment (the base) equals the height of the given triangle. This is because the height is a perpendicular line to the base, if the base is fixed, the height can only go above or below it.

132. The answer is (C). This is a typical right isosceles triangle. Hence, the ratio between the longer hypotenuse to the shorter leg must be $\sqrt{2}$ to 1.

133. The answer is (C). Since $\frac{1}{2} \times$ base $\times (x + 3) = 2x^2 + 5x - 3$, we get **base** $= 4x - 2$ by performing a long division.

134. The answer is (B). Either using the power of points or Pythagorean Theorem, we conclude that CD is cut into 2 and 32. Hence, $OE = 15$.

135. The answer is (B). Let $DB = k$. Then, $k^2 = (\frac{3}{2})^2 + (5 - \frac{3\sqrt{3}}{2})^2 = 34 - 15\sqrt{3}$. Thus, $a + b + c = 34 + 15 + 3 = 34 + 18 = 52$.

136. The answer is (B). Regardless of whether $\overline{BC}$ is a diameter, we always get $m\angle ACB = 45°$, according to the ratio between the inscribed angle and the central angle.

137. The answer is (B). $m\angle AEB = \frac{90° - 40°}{2} = 25°$.

138. The answer is (C). The height of a smaller equilateral triangle, six of which consist of the regular hexagon, can be written as $2\sqrt{3}$. Hence, the side length must be 4.

139. The answer is (D). According to the power of points, $4 \times 5 = 2 \times CE$, so $CE = 10$.

140. The answer is (D). According to the power of points, we get $4 \times 5 = 2 \times CE$, so $CE = 10$.

141. The answer is (A). This is the definition of perpendicular bisector. A perpendicular bisector is a line or a plane that is perpendicular to and bisects (divides into two equal parts) a line segment. In other words, it is a line that goes through the midpoint of a line segment and is perpendicular to that line segment. The line segment is the segment that is bisected.

142. The answer is (C). Remember that the circumdiameter of a right triangle is always its hypotenuse. This can be proven by drawing a right triangle and marking the circumcenter, which is the midpoint of the hypotenuse. It's clear that the hypotenuse is the longest distance between any two points on the triangle, and it goes through the circumcenter, which is the center of its circumcircle.

This theorem is known as the circumdiameter of a right triangle theorem and can be used to find the length of the hypotenuse of a right triangle if the lengths of the legs are known. It also can be used to prove properties of right triangles.

143. The answer is (D). It is clear that O is its centroid. Hence, $AO : OA' = 2 : 1$. Let $AO = 2k$ and $OA' = k$, such that $2k + k = 3k = 12$. Thus, $k = 4$. We conclude that $AO = 2k = 8$.

144. The answer is (C). Menelaus' theorem is a statement in Euclidean geometry that states that in any triangle and any transversal that intersects the three sides of the triangle, the product of the directed ratios of the segments of the transversal to the corresponding segments of the triangle stays constant. According to the theorem, $\frac{AF}{BF} \times \frac{BC}{CE} \times \frac{ED}{AD} = 1$. Thus, $\frac{ED}{AD} = \frac{1}{4}$. Hence, $\frac{AD}{ED} = \frac{4}{1}$, so $m + n = 4 + 1 = 5$.

145. The answer is (C). A regular decagon has 10 vertices to choose. Hence, out of 10 vertices, we must choose 4 vertices to form a quadrilateral. There are $\binom{10}{4}$ number of quadrilaterals formed, where $\binom{10}{4} = \frac{10 \cdot 9 \cdot 8 \cdot 7}{4 \cdot 3 \cdot 2 \cdot 1} = 210$.

146. The answer is (A). Given a cyclic quadrilateral, any three adjacent vertices form a triangle circumscribed about the same circle. It is easy to find out that the circumcenters of the three triangles formed by the three adjacent vertices of a cyclic quadrilateral all coincide at a single point. This is because the circumcenter of a triangle is the center of the circle that circumscribes the triangle and since these three triangles are all tangent to the same circle, so their circumcenters will be at the center of that circle.

This property of a cyclic quadrilateral is known as the "Common Internal Tangents" or "Common Internal Secant" theorem. It is useful in solving geometric problems and proving properties of cyclic quadrilaterals.

147. The answer is (B). Since the height is 12, we can deduce that the side length must be $8\sqrt{3}$. Thus, the area must be $\frac{\sqrt{3}}{4}(8\sqrt{3})^2 = \frac{\sqrt{3}}{4} \times (64 \cdot 3) = 48\sqrt{3}$. Hence, $a\sqrt{b} = 48\sqrt{3}$, so $a + b = 48 + 3 = 51$.

148. The answer is (C). Cut the chord into half by drawing a diameter passing through its midpoint. Then, we can easily deduce that $r^2 = 208$ by Pythagorean Theorem. The area of circle can be written as $\pi(r^2) = 208\pi$. Thus, $k = 208$.

149. The answer is (D). Let the centroid be R. Then, $AR = BR = 4$, and $PR = QR = 2$. Since the two given medians form a right angle, we conclude that $[ARB] = 8$, $[AQR] = [BPR] = 4$. Since $CQ = AQ$ and $CP = BP$, we also conclude that $[CQR] = [CPR] = 4$. Therefore, the area of $\triangle ABC$ must be 24.

150. The answer is (B). Let D be the perpendicular foot from A to $\overline{BC}$. Drawing ω_1 and ω_2 nicely, we get the two points of intersection are A and D. Since $AD = 12$, we conclude that the answer is (B), using circumdiameters' diameters as right triangles' hypotenuses.

Memo

The Essential Workbook for

Geometry

초판발행 2023년 2월 3일

저자 유하림
발행인 최영민
발행처 헤르몬하우스
주소 경기도 파주시 신촌로 16
전화 031-8071-0088
팩스 031-942-8688
전자우편 hermonh@naver.com
출판등록 2015년 3월 27일
등록번호 제406-2015-31호

© 유하림 2023, Printed in Korea.

ISBN 979-11-92520-25-4 (53410)